GRADE 1

Alyza

Cali Treasures

Practice Book

Mc Graw Hill Macmillan/McGraw-Hill

Contents

Contents

Unit 1 • All About Us

Contents

Unit 2 • Our Families, Our Neighbors

Contents

Unit 3 • Have Fun

Contents

Unit 4 • Let's Team Up

Contents

Unit 5 • Nature Watch

Contents

Unit 6 • Adventures

Start Smart

Name ______________________

Say each picture name. Then write an **m** or **s** below the picture if its name begins with the **m** or **s** sound.

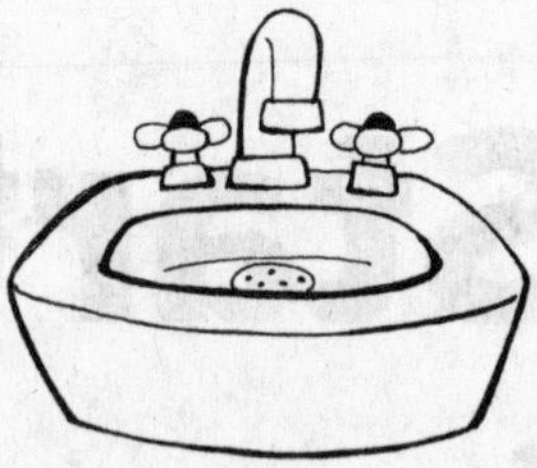

Write an **m** or **s** to complete the words.

_____ op

_____ ock

We can [paint set].

High-Frequency Vocabulary:
like, can, the, I, we

We Can

I like the [sun].

CA **R 1.11** Read common, irregular sight words (e.g., *the*, *have*, *said*, *come*, *give*, *of*).

We can [picture of a shovel digging].

2

I like the [picture of raindrops].

3

© Macmillan/McGraw-Hill

CA **R 1.11** Read common, irregular sight words (e.g., *the, have, said, come, give, of*).

Name ______________________

Say each picture name. Then write a **p** or **t** below the picture if its name begins with the **p** or **t** sound.

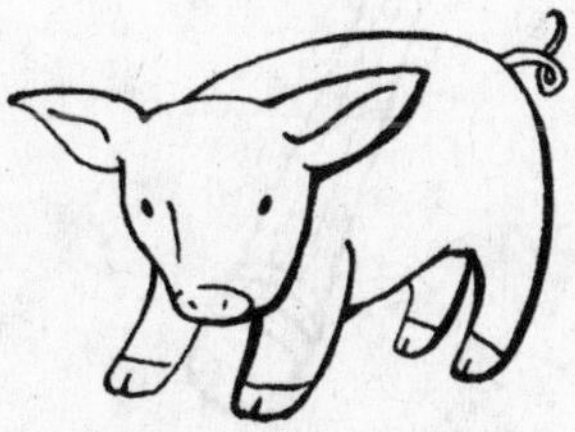

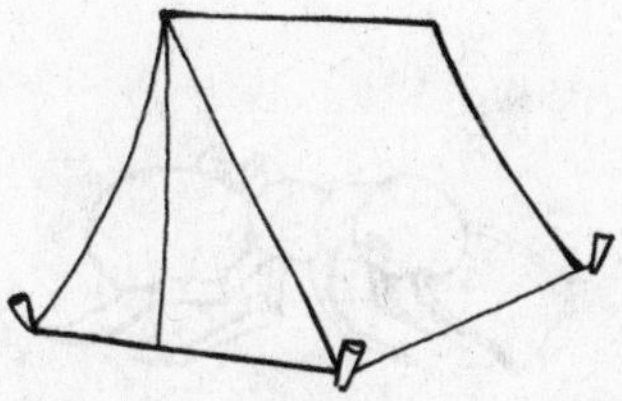

Write a **p** or **t** to complete the words.

____ ig

____ ent

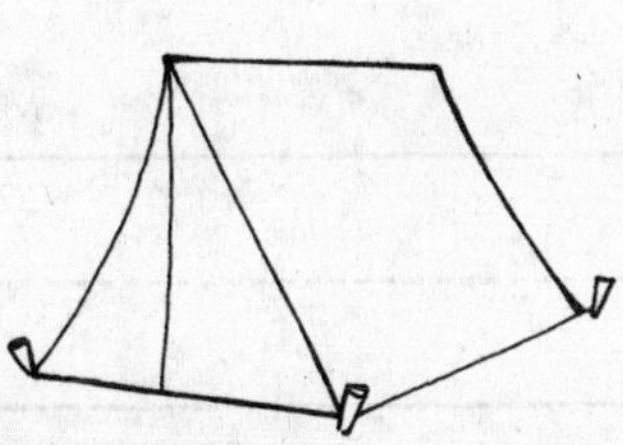

Name ________________________

Say each picture name. Then write an a below the picture if its name begins with the a sound.

Trace the word **at**. Then practice writing the word **at**.

at

Trace the word **an**. Then practice writing the word **an**.

an

We see the 🦀.

High-Frequency Vocabulary:
we, go, to, the, see

4

We Like to Go

We go to the .

1

R 1.11 Read common, irregular sight words (e.g., *the, have, said, come, give, of*).

We see the [frogs].

2

We go to the [beach].

3

CA **R 1.11** Read common, irregular sight words (e.g., *the*, *have*, *said*, *come*, *give*, *of*).

Name ______________________________

Say each picture name. Then write a **c** or **n** below the picture if its name begins with the **c** or **n** sound.

Write an **a** to complete the words. Then read them.

c ____ t   m ____ n

c ____ n   m ____ p

Name ____________________

Say each picture name. Then write **f** or **h** below the picture if its name begins with the **f** or **h** sound.

______

______

______

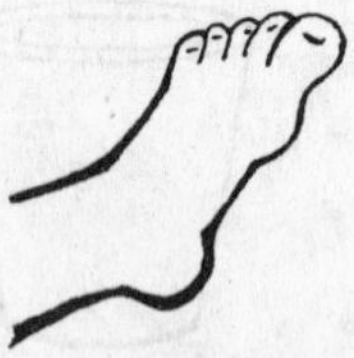
______

______

______

Trace the word **if**. Then practice writing the word **if**.

if ____________________

Write an **f** or **h** to complete the word.

______at 

He is .

High-Frequency Vocabulary:
you, is, have

4

We Have

I have a .

1

CA **R 1.11** Read common, irregular sight words (e.g., *the, have, said, come, give, of*).

He is 

.

2

You have a  .

3

 **R 1.11** Read common, irregular sight words (e.g., *the*, *have*, *said*, *come*, *give*, *of*).

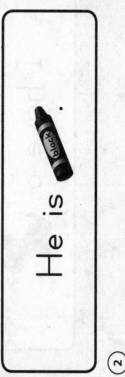

Name ____________________________________

Say each picture name. Then write an **i** below the picture if its name begins with the **i** sound.

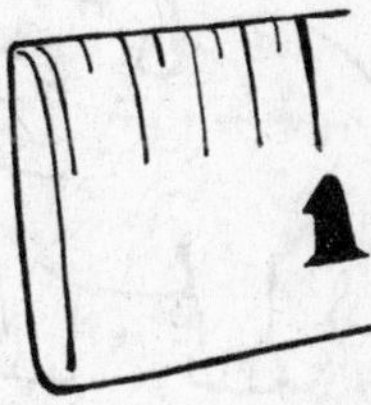

Trace the word **in**. Then practice writing the word **in**.

in

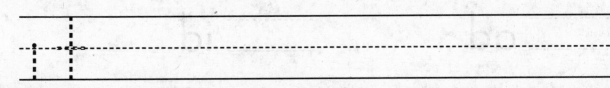

Trace the word **it**. Then practice writing the word **it**.

it

Name ______________________________

Say each picture name. Then write a **d** or **r** below the picture if its name begins with the **d** or **r** sound.

Write **r** to complete the words. Then read the words.

____ at ____ an

Write **d** to complete the words. Then read the words.

____ ad ____ id

CA R 1.0 Word Analysis, Fluency, and Systematic Vocabulary Development

Name ____________________

Say each picture name. Then write a **b** or **l** below the picture if its name begins with the **b** or **l** sound.

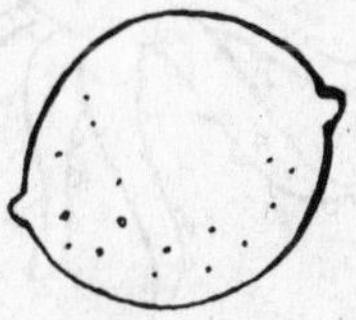

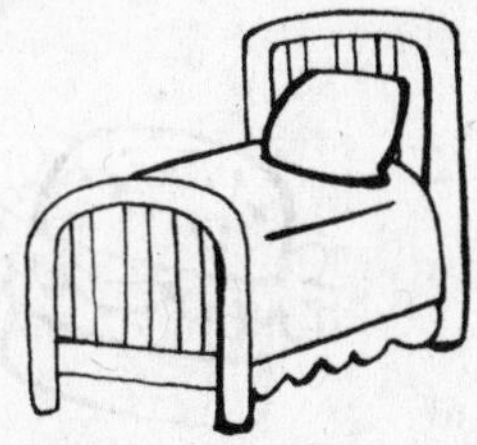

Write **b** or **l** to complete the words.

____ all 

____ ips 

Name ______________________________

Say each picture name. Then write an **o** below the picture if its name begins with the **o** sound.

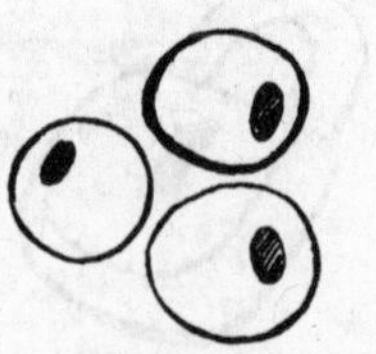

Trace the word **on**. Then practice writing the word **on**.

on

Write an **o** to complete the word.

____x

CA R 1.0 Word Analysis, Fluency, and Systematic Vocabulary Development

We can play [soccer picture].

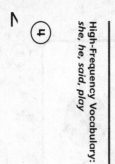

High-Frequency Vocabulary:
she, he, said, play

4

We Can

He said, "I can [reading picture]."

1

R 1.11 Read common, irregular sight words (e.g., *the*, *have*, *said*, *come*, *give*, *of*).

She said, "I can ."

2

We can play .

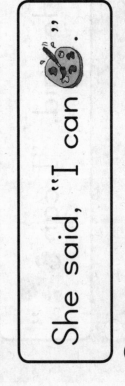

3

CA **R 1.11** Read common, irregular sight words (e.g., *the*, *have*, *said*, *come*, *give*, *of*).

Name ________________________________

Say each picture name. Then write a **k** below the picture if its name begins with the **k** sound.

Say each picture name. Then write a **ck** below the picture if its name ends with the **k** sound.

Use 2 letters to make new words.

ki ________

si ________

Use 1 letter to make new words.

________ ick

________ ick

Name ______________________

Say each picture name. Then write an **e** below the picture if its name begins with the **e** sound.

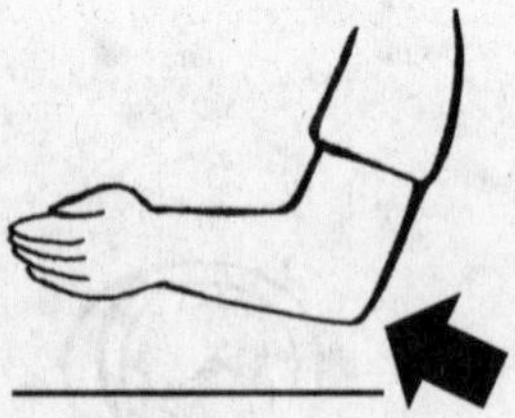

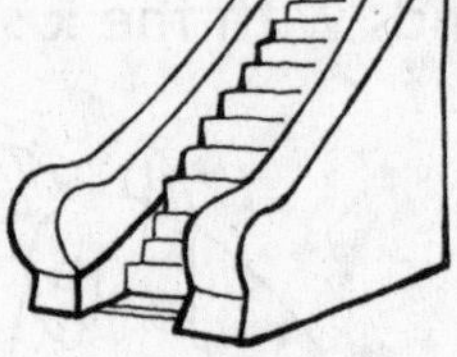

Trace the word **Ed**. Then, practice writing the word **Ed**.

Ed

Write an **e** to complete the word. Then read it.

___gg

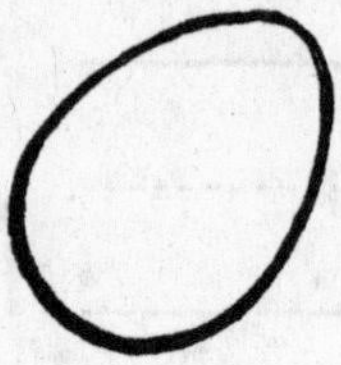

We like the  .

High-Frequency Vocabulary:
here, are, what, do, have, is, for

Here We Are!

What can we do?

R 1.11 Read common, irregular sight words (e.g., *the, have, said, come, give, of*).

(2) We can have .

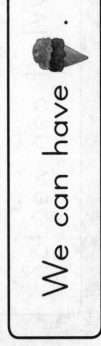

What is this for? (3)

R 1.11 Read common, irregular sight words (e.g., *the*, *have*, *said*, *come*, *give*, *of*).

Name ____________________

Say each picture name. Then write a **g** or **w** below the picture if its name begins with the **g** or **w** sound.

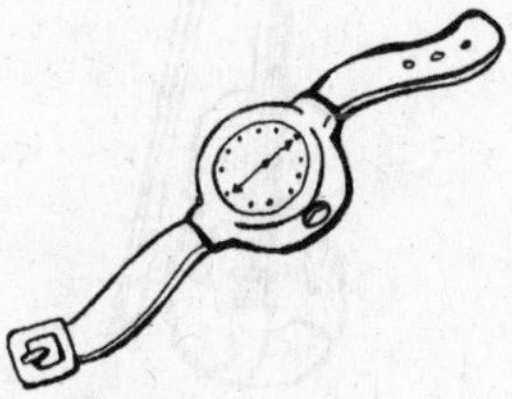

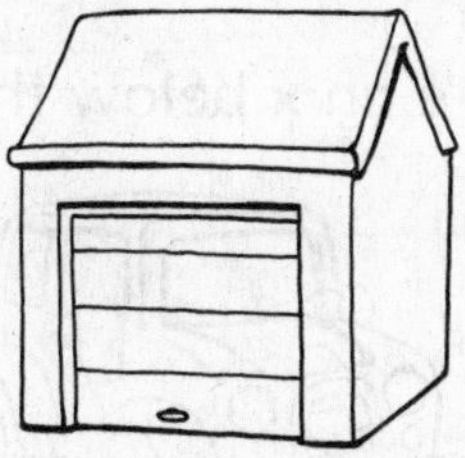

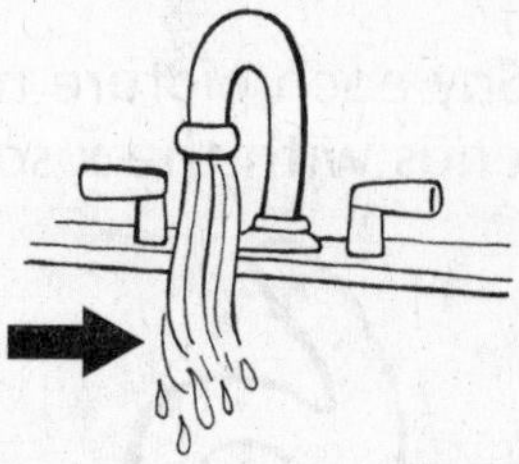

Write **g**, **w**, **s**, or **b** to complete the words. Then read them.

___et ___et

___et ___et

Name ______________________________

Say each picture name. Then write a **v** or **j** below the picture if its name begins with the **v** or **j** sound.

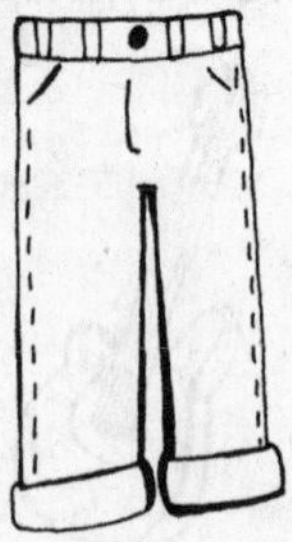

Say each picture name. Then write an **x** below the picture if its name ends with the **x** sound.

Write **v**, **j**, or **x** to complete the words. Then read them.

_____an

_____et

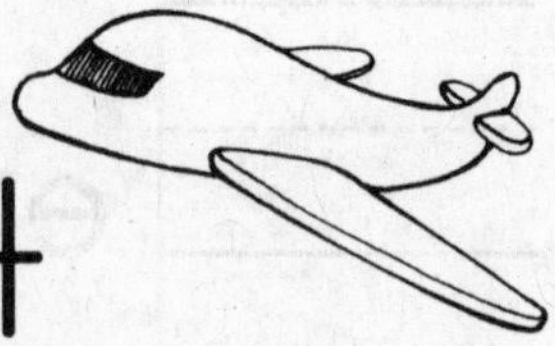

bo_____

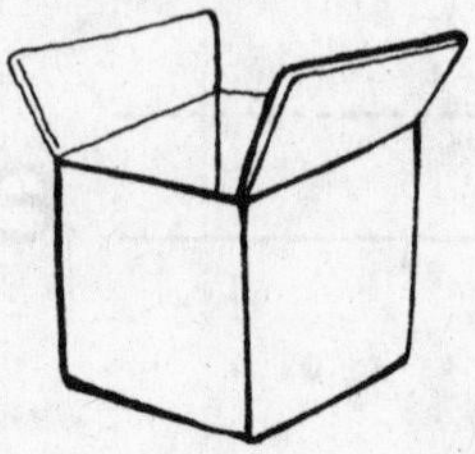

She has a bone.

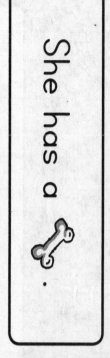

High-Frequency Vocabulary:
do, my, look, is, was, has

Look and See

Do you see my dog.

CA **R 1.11** Read common, irregular sight words (e.g., *the, have, said, come, give, of*).

Was my  here?

2

Look, here she is!

3

CA **R 1.11** Read common, irregular sight words (e.g., *the, have, said, come, give, of*).

Name ______________________________

Say each picture name. Then write a **u** below the picture if its name begins with the **u** sound.

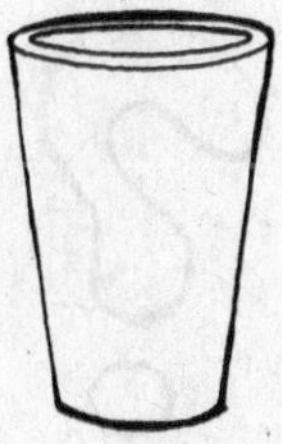
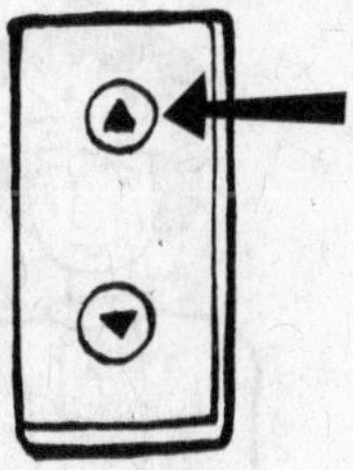

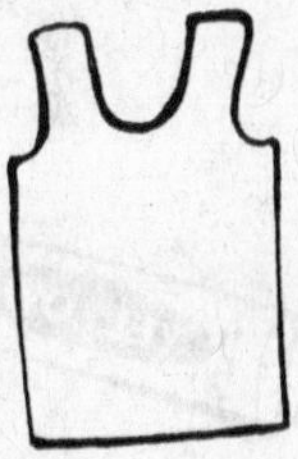

Trace the word **up**. Then practice writing the word **up**.

up

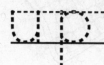

Trace the word **us**. Then practice writing the word **us**.

us

Name ____________________

Say each picture name. Then write a **q**, **y**, or **z** below the picture if its name begins with the **q**, **y**, or **z** sound.

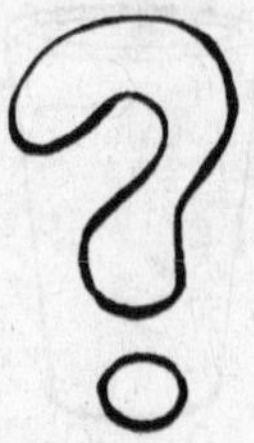

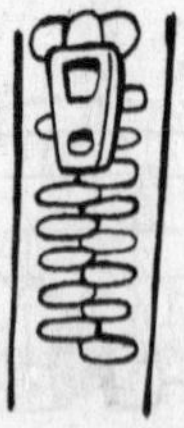

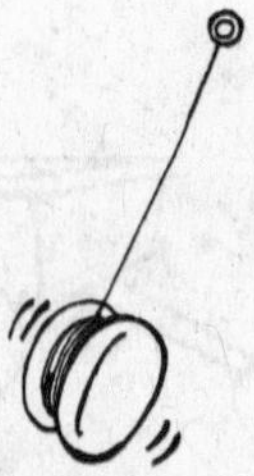

Write **q**, **y**, or **z** to complete the words.

____ero 

____uilt 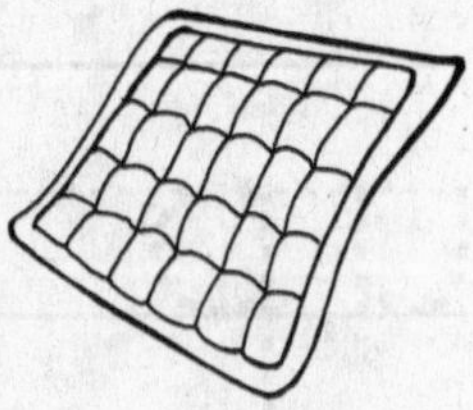

____arn 

Name ______________________________

Read the word. Circle the picture that it names.

1. cat

2. pan

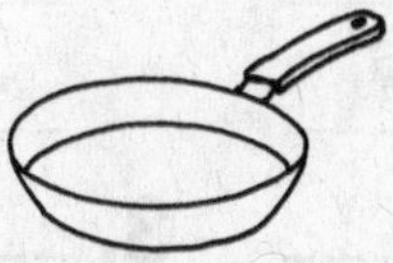  

3. man

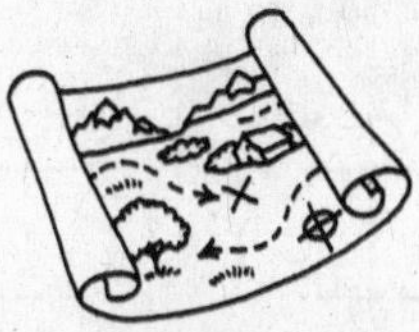  

4. sat

5. fan

6. Write a sentence using some of the words.

____

____

CA **R 1.4** Distinguish initial, medial, and final sounds in single-syllable words.

Name ______________________________

man	cat	hat	mat
ran	can	up	not

Write the words that end with an.

1. ____________ **2.** ____________ **3.** ____________

Write the words that end with at.

4. ____________ **5.** ____________ **6.** ____________

Write the other words.

7. ____________ **8.** ____________

CA LC 1.8 Spell three- and four-letter short-vowel words and grade-level-appropriate sight words correctly.

Name ________________________________

Complete each sentence.
Use one of the words in the box.

up	not	jump

1. I can ______________.

2. The cat ran ______________.

3. The cat is ______________ little.

4. Write your own sentence using a word from the box.

____

CA **R 1.11** Read common, irregular sight words (e.g., *the, have, said, come, give, of*).

Name ________________________________

A sentence is a group of words that tells a whole idea.

Example: The cat can jump.

Circle the sentences.

1. She sat down.

2. We can jump up.

3. Ran here.

4. Pat can do this.

5. Like to.

Name ____________________

Circle the word that names each picture.

Then write the word.

1. 

cat cats

2. 

man map

3. 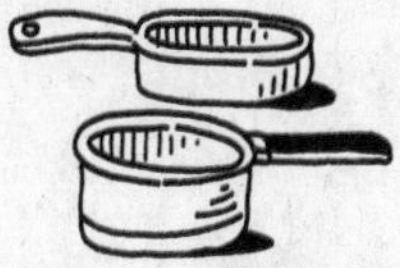

pan pans

4. 

rats rat

5. 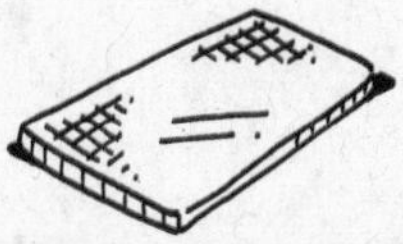

mat mats

6. 

can cans

7. 

fans fan

8. 

hat hats

CA **R 1.14** Read inflectional forms (e.g., *-s*, *-ed*, *-ing*) and root words (e.g., *look*, *looked*, *looking*).

Name ____________________

Look at each set of words.
One word in each set is spelled correctly.
Use a pencil to fill in the circle in front of that word.
Sample A is done for you.

Sample A:

○ A. mann
● B. man
○ C. maan

1. ○ A. cat
○ B. kat
○ C. catt

2. ○ A. haat
○ B. het
○ C. hat

3. ○ A. mot
○ B. mat
○ C. matt

4. ○ A. ran
○ B. raan
○ C. rann

5. ○ A. can
○ B. caan
○ C. kan

6. ○ A. upp
○ B. up
○ C. upt

7. ○ A. ont
○ B. nott
○ C. not

CA LC 1.8 Spell three- and four-letter short-vowel words and grade-level-appropriate sight words correctly.

Name ______________________________

As you read Pam and Sam, fill in the Character Chart.

Pam Can	Sam Can

How does the Character Chart help you remember the beginning, middle, and end of Pam and Sam?

Name ________________________________

Look at the pictures. Read the story.

Nat is a cat.
Nat can go up.
Nat can go down.
Pam and Sam look for Nat.
Pam is sad.
Where is Nat?

Write T if the sentence is true.
Write F if the sentence is false.

1. Nat is a cat. ____

2. Nat can go up and down. ____

3. Pam is sad. ____

4. Nat is in the  . ____

5. Nat is in the  . ____

CA R 3.1 Identify and describe the elements of plot, setting, and character(s) in a story, as well as the story's beginning, middle, and ending.

Name ______________________

A sentence is a group of words that tells a whole idea.

Every sentence begins with a capital letter.

Write each sentence correctly.

1. we can nap here.

2. she ran and ran.

3. sam said to go up.

4. do not jump.

Add words to make this a sentence.

5. nan has

Name ____________________

As I read, I will pay attention to the intonation.

"I can jump," said Pat. "I can jump up
09 and down."
11 "I can jump," said Sam. "I can jump up
20 and down."
22 "I can jump, too!" said Cam. "I can
30 jump up and down."
34 "I can not jump," said Dan.
40 "I can tap!" said Dan. 45

Comprehension Check

1. What can Pat, Sam, and Cam do?

2. What can Dan do?

	Words Read	–	Number of Errors	=	Words Correct Score
First Read		–		=	
Second Read		–		=	

CA **R 1.16** Read aloud with fluency in a manner that sounds like natural speech.

Name ______________________

Photographs are pictures that show people, animals, and things in real life.

Look at the picture.
Read the sentence that tells about the picture.

Look! My little cat is here.

Write your own sentence about the picture.

____

____

Name ______________________________

Say the name of each picture.
Circle the picture if you hear the sound of short a.

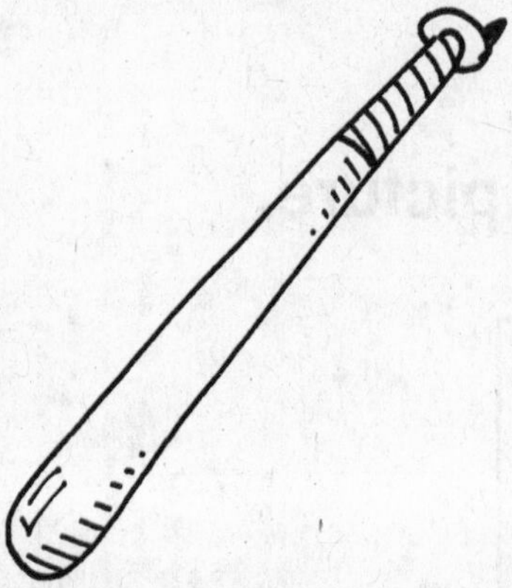

CA R 1.4 Distinguish initial, medial, and final sounds in single-syllable words.

Name ____________________

dad	sad	nap	tap	sack
back	man	cat	too	it

Look at the picture. Write the correct word.

Words with **ad**

1. ____________________

2. ____________________

Words with **ap**

3. ____________________

4. ____________________

Words with **ack**

5. ____________________

6. ____________________

CA **LC 1.8** Spell three- and four-letter short-vowel words and grade-level-appropriate sight words correctly.

Name ________________________

Fill in the sentences using the words in the box.

too	It	over

1. ____________ is in the box.

2. You have fun, ____________!

3. It is ____________ us.

CA **R 1.11** Read common, irregular sight words (e.g., *the, have, said, come, give, of*).

Name ______________________________

The words in a sentence have to be in the right order.

The order has to make sense.

Correct: Sam ran over my cap.

Not correct: ran cap Sam my over.

Circle the sentences that have the words in the right order.

1. Dan jumps over the hat.

2. it We over jump.

3. Pat tags Dan.

4. She plays tag, too.

5. ran Sam here back.

Name ______________________________

Circle the word that completes each sentence. Then write the word on the line.

1. Sam ________________.

   nap   naps

2. Sam and Pam ________________.

   play   plays

3. Pam can ________________.

   pack   packs

4. Pam ________________ go with Sam.

   can   cans

5. Pam ________________ at Sam.

   look   looks

CA **R 1.14** Read inflectional forms (e.g., *-s, -ed, -ing*) and root words (e.g., *look, looked, looking*).

Name ______________________

dad	nap	sad	tap	sack
back	it	too	man	cat

Mark an X on the line next to the word that is spelled correctly.

1. apn ______ nap ______ anp ______
2. too ______ oto ______ oot ______
3. dda ______ dad ______ daa ______
4. cta ______ cat ______ tac ______
5. kabc ______ bakc ______ back ______

In each row put an X on the word that does not belong. Then write the spelling word.

6. mad	sad	go	______
7. tap	see	rap	______
8. has	pack	sack	______

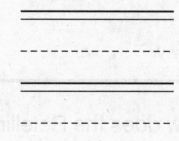

CA LC 1.8 Spell three- and four-letter short-vowel words and grade-level-appropriate sight words correctly.

Name ______________________________

As you read I Can Too!, fill in the Retelling Chart.

First

Next

Last

How does the Retelling Chart help you retell I Can Too!?

CA R 2.1 Identify text that uses sequence or other logical order.

Name ______________________________

Look at the pictures.
Write <u>1</u>, <u>2</u>, and <u>3</u> for each column of pictures to show the order in which things happen.

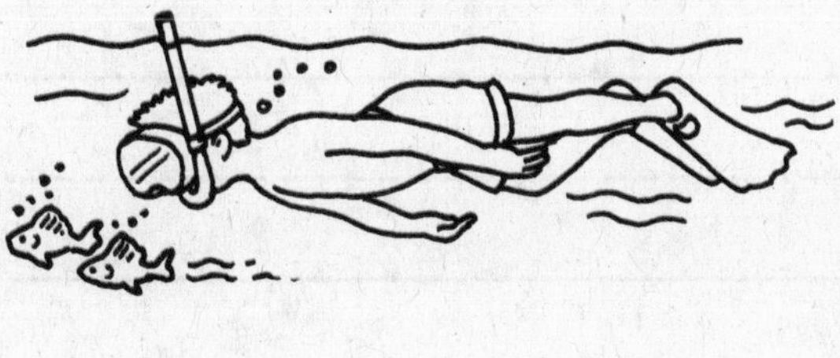

CA R 2.1 Identify text that uses sequence or other logical order.

Name ______________________________

The words in a sentence must make sense.

A sentence ends with a period.

Look at the sentences. Write C if a sentence is correct.

Fix the others by writing the words in order.

1. not Pam can go.

2. He has the map.

3. The cat sat on it.

4. down jumps She up and.

5. Sam can see Hal.

Name ______________________________

As I read, I will pay attention to pauses for sentence punctuation.

"I can not nap," said Rat. "Can you, Cat?"
09 "I can nap," said Cat.
14 "I can not," said Rat. "Can you nap, Bat?"
23 "Nap? Yes, I can nap, too," said Bat.
31 "I can not nap," said Rat. "I can play tag!" 41

Comprehension Check

1. Who could nap?

2. Who could not nap?

	Words Read	–	Number of Errors	=	Words Correct Score
First Read		–		=	
Second Read		–		=	

CA **R 1.16** Read aloud with fluency in a manner that sounds like natural speech.

Name ______________________________

Labels give information about a picture.

Look at the picture. Read the labels.

Write the word that completes each sentence.

1. The man has a ______________.

2. Pam has a ______________.

3. The cat has a ______________.

4. Sam has a ______________.

Name ______________________________

The letter **i** stands for the middle sound in **big** and **fin.**

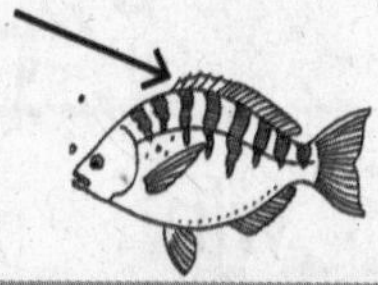

Read the words in the box. Then write the word that names each picture.

pig	kid	pin	sit

1. ____________

2. ____________

3. ____________

4. ____________

CA **R 1.10** Generate the sounds from all the letters and letter patterns, including consonant blends and long- and short-vowel patterns (i.e., phonograms), and blend those sounds into recognizable words.

Name ______________________

Read the spelling words.

pin	win	hit	sit	miss
kiss	sad	nap	be	run

Write the words that end with it.

1. ____________ 2. ____________

Write the words that end with in.

3. ____________ 4. ____________

Write the words that end with iss.

5. ____________ 6. ____________

Write the other words.

7. ____________ 8. ____________

9. ____________ 10. ____________

CA **LC 1.8** Spell three- and four-letter short-vowel words and grade-level-appropriate sight words correctly.

Name ______________________________

Write the word from the box that completes each sentence. Circle the picture that goes with the sentence.

be	ride	run

1. Nan will ______________ here.

2. My cat can ______________ here with me.

3. I can ______________ with Nat.

CA **R 1.11** Read common, irregular sight words (e.g., *the, have, said, come, give, of*).

Practice

Grammar: Statements

Name ______________________________

A statement tells something.

Example: Wag is little.

Draw a line under the statements.

1. Wag naps and naps.

2. Digs too

3. Wag has my cap.

4. He runs to me.

5. Rides

6. Wag and I play.

CA LC 1.4 Distinguish between declarative, exclamatory, and interrogative sentences.

Name ____________________

Some words end in the same two consonants.

bi**ll** Ja**zz** pa**ss**

Read each sentence.
Underline the word that ends with the same two consonants. Write the word on the line.

1. Matt runs to his little cat.

2. Pam rides to the hill.

3. I kiss my Dad.

4. The mitt is on the ride.

Practice

Spelling: Short *i*

Name ______________________________

pin	win	hit	sit
miss	kiss	be	run

Find the spelling words in the puzzle. Draw a circle around each word.

a	o	m	i	s	s	r	f	l
g	u	c	e	y	k	w	i	n
s	i	t	o	v	l	j	z	x
j	u	f	p	i	n	m	k	u
y	b	e	k	u	z	l	a	v
f	v	p	c	l	h	i	t	o
k	i	s	s	a	r	f	k	x
u	c	o	l	r	u	n	e	j

CA **LC 1.8** Spell three- and four-letter short-vowel words and grade-level-appropriate sight words correctly.

Name ___________________________

As you read How You Grew, fill in the Retelling Chart.

First

↓

Next

↓

Then

↓

Last

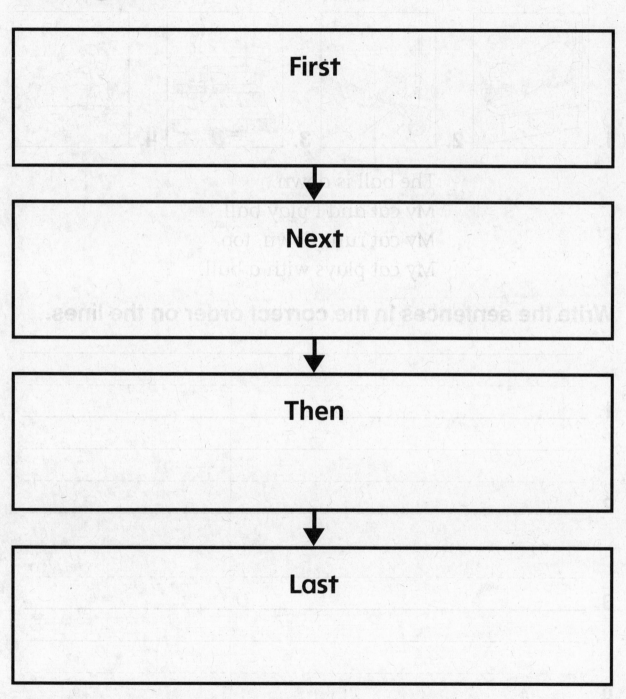

How does the Retelling Chart help you retell How You Grew?

CA **R 2.1** Identify text that uses sequence or other logical order.

Name ________________________________

Look at the story pictures.
Read the sentences about the story.

1. 
2. 
3. 
4. 

The ball is down.
My cat and I play ball.
My cat runs down, too.
My cat plays with a ball.

Write the sentences in the correct order on the lines.

1. ________________________________

2. ________________________________

3. ________________________________

4. ________________________________

CA R 2.1 Identify text that uses sequence or other logical order.

Name ______________________________

A statement is a sentence that tells something. A statement begins with a capital letter and ends with a period.

Read each pair of statements.

Circle the statement that is correct.

1. She runs and jumps.

We jump, too

2. he sits down

Jack rides with me.

3. My cap is in here.

Pam can not see it

4. Sam can play this.

You can do it

CA LC 1.4 Distinguish between declarative, exclamatory, and interrogative sentences.

Name ____________________

As I read, I will pay attention to the exclamation marks.

Big Max is a big cat. Big Max can sit.
10 Big Max can dig. Dig, Max, dig!
17 He can lick his back, too!
23 Big Max can play and run. Run, Max, run!
32 Big Max will not hit. 37

Comprehension Check

1. What is Big Max?

2. What are two things Big Max can do?

	Words Read	–	Number of Errors	=	Words Correct Score
First Read		–		=	
Second Read		–		=	

CA **R 1.16** Read aloud with fluency in a manner that sounds like natural speech.

Name ________________________________

The **title** of a book is the name of the book.
The **author** of a book writes the story.
The **illustrator** makes the pictures.

Look at the book cover. Answer the questions.

1. Who wrote the book?

____

2. Who made the picture?

____

3. What is the title of the book?

____

4. What picture is on the cover?

____

Name ______________________

Blend the first two letters to read each word.

flag **cl**ap **bl**ack **bl**ock **cl**ip **cl**ock

Use the words in the box to name each picture.

1.  ______________

2.  ______________

3.  ______________

4.  ______________

5. 

____

6.  ______________

CA **R 1.10** Generate the sounds from all the letters and letter patterns, including consonant blends and long- and short-vowel patterns (i.e., phonograms), and blend those sounds into recognizable words.

Name ______________________________

clip	plan	flag	flip	black
slip	win	sit	come	good

Look at the pictures. Combine one word part from each box to make a spelling word.

bl	cl	fl

ack	ag	ip

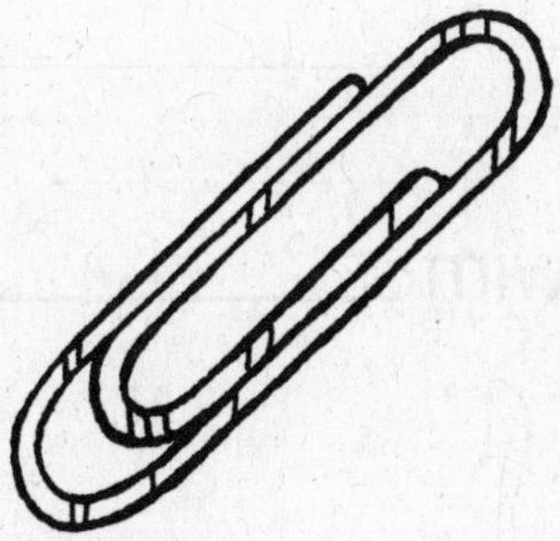

1. ______________ **2.** ______________

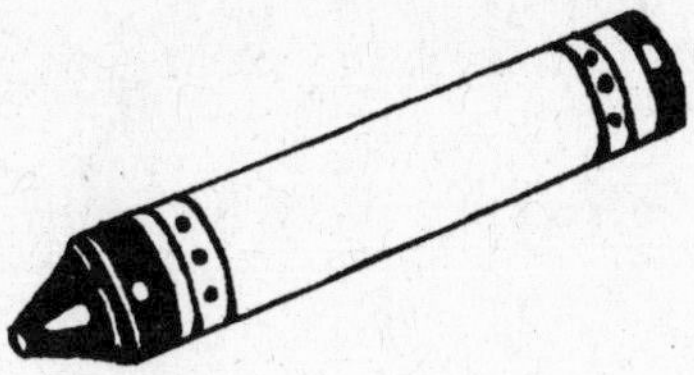

3. ______________ **4.** ______________

CA **LC 1.8** Spell three- and four-letter short-vowel words and grade-level-appropriate sight words correctly.

Name ____________________________

Practice

High-Frequency Words/Vocabulary

Write the word from the box that completes each sentence. Circle the picture that goes with each sentence.

come	good	pull	down

1. It can ______________ a cart.

2. It can swim ______________ in the pond.

3. She will ______________ if you call her.

4. He is ______________ at sleeping.

CA R 1.11 Read common, irregular sight words (e.g., *the, have, said, come, give, of*).

Name ______________________________

A question is a sentence that asks something.

Example: Where is that cat?

A. Write Q next to each question. Do not write anything if the sentence is not a question.

1. Is the cat there? ____________
2. The cat is not here. ____________
3. Did the cat go up? ____________
4. Did the cat come down? ____________
5. I did not see that cat. ____________
6. Where can it be? ____________

B. Write a question on the line.

____

CA LC 1.4 Distinguish between declarative, exclamatory, and interrogative sentences.

Name ______________________________

When **'s** is added to a word, it means that something belongs to that person or thing.

Circle the correct word and write it on the line.

1. This is ______________ pet.

Fran Fran's

2. This is ______________ bag.

Gram's Gram

3. This is the ______________ trap.

crab crab's

4. This is ______________ cat.

Mr. Tran Mr. Tran's

5. This is ______________ crib.

Jim's Jim

Name ____________________

A. Pick a letter from the box to make a spelling word. Then write the word.

o	i	a	d

1. pl ____ n ____________
2. sl ____ p ____________
3. fl ____ p ____________
4. cl ____ p ____________
5. c ____ me ____________
6. fl ____ g ____________

B. Circle the two spelling words that are correct. Then write the word.

black bleck gode good bluck

7. ____________ 8. ____________

CA LC 1.8 Spell three- and four-letter short-vowel words and grade-level-appropriate sight words correctly.

Name ______________________________

As you read Flip, fill in the Beginning, Middle, and End Chart.

Beginning

↓

Middle

↓

End

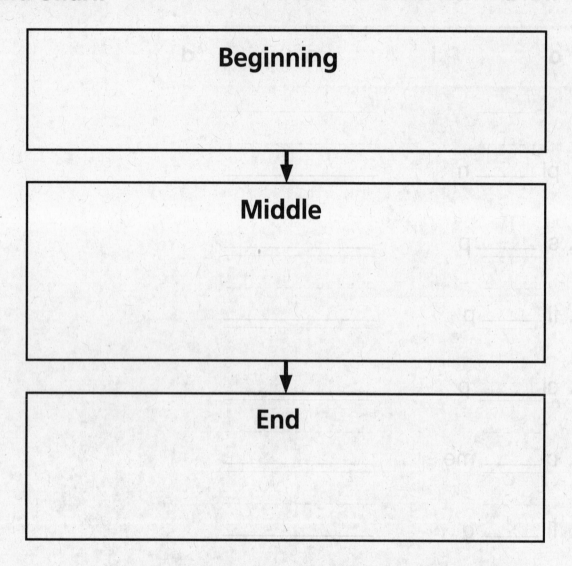

How does the Beginning, Middle, and End Chart help you better understand Flip?

CA **R 3.1** Identify and describe the elements of plot, setting, and character(s) in a story, as well as the story's beginning, middle, and ending.

Read the story.

The Baby Bunny

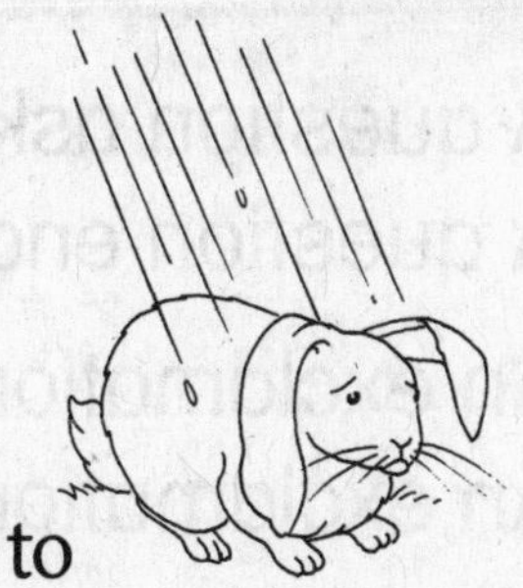

All the baby bunnies were sleeping in their nest. One baby woke up. He planned to have some fun. The bunny left the nest.

What a big place he saw! The bunny hopped and jumped. He had a good time. Then the rain fell. The baby bunny wished he was safe in his cozy nest.

Just then, he saw his mom. She was calling his name. The baby bunny hopped to his mom. They went back home. He was glad.

Read the sentences. Write B for the beginning sentences, M for the middle ones, and E for the end ones.

1. The rain came. ______
2. The bunny went home. ______
3. The bunny left the nest. ______
4. The bunny had a good time. ______

CA R 3.1 Identify and describe the elements of plot, setting, and character(s) in a story, as well as the story's beginning, middle, and ending.

Name ______________________

Practice

Grammar: Questions and Exclamations

A question asks something.
A question ends with a question mark.

An exclamation shows strong feelings.
An exclamation ends with an exclamation mark.

Write each sentence correctly. Write C if a sentence is correct.

1. What is on the mat!

2. That is big!

3. Grab the cat quick?

4. Can we come in!

5. Is this a trap?

CA **LC 1.4** Distinguish between declarative, exclamatory, and interrogative sentences.

Name ______________________________

As I read, I will pay attention to the exclamation marks.

Little Pat sat in his class.
06 He had to pack his bag with caps.
14 "I can not fill my bag!" said Pat.
22 "It has ten cans in it!"
28 Jim had a sack. "Fill my sack with the caps!"
38 Little Pat was glad. 42

Comprehension Check

1. What did Little Pat want to put in his bag?
2. Who helped Little Pat?

	Words Read	–	Number of Errors	=	Words Correct Score
First Read		–		=	
Second Read		–		=	

CA **R 1.16** Read aloud with fluency in a manner that sounds like natural speech.

Name ______________________________

Practice

Text Feature: Lists

A **list** is a series of things written in order.

Pets can

1. 

2. 

3. 

4. 

Read the question. Draw a line to the answer.

1. What pet likes to nap?

2. What pet can beg?

3. What pet can wag?

4. What pet likes to play?

Name ________________________

Practice

Phonics: End Blends

Sometimes consonants form a **blend**. You can hear each consonant sound in a **final blend**.

ha**nd** pa**st**

Say the word. Draw a line under the final blend. Write the final blend on the line. Circle the picture.

1. a n t ________

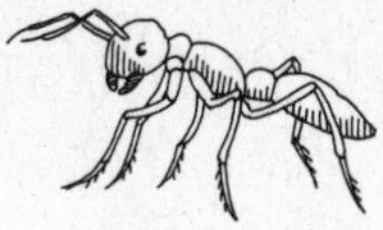

2. l i s t ________

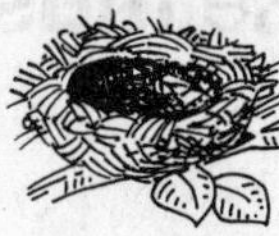
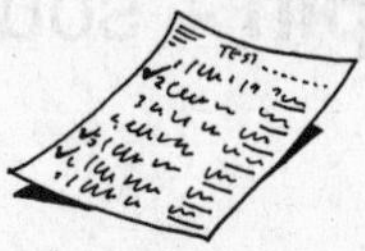

3. b a n d ________

4. r i n k ________

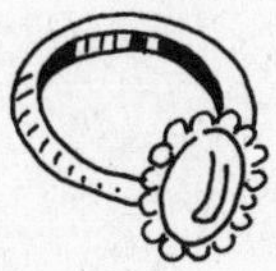

CA **R 1.10** Generate the sounds from all the letters and letter patterns, including consonant blends and long- and short-vowel patterns (i.e., phonograms), and blend those sounds into recognizable words.

Name ______________________________

land	sand	fast	past	sink
sing	black	flip	use	very

Use the clues to write a spelling word on the line.

1. starts like **for** + sounds like **last** ______________

2. starts like **sip** + sounds like **link** ______________

3. starts like **pin** + sounds like **mast** ______________

4. starts like **sip** + sounds like **hand** ______________

5. starts like **flat** + sounds like **sip** ______________

6. starts like **last** + sounds like **hand** ______________

CA **LC 1.8** Spell three- and four-letter short-vowel words and grade-level-appropriate sight words correctly.

Name ________________________________

Use a word from the box to complete each sentence.

very	help	use	now

1. Tom can ______________ Nan ride.

2. Look! What she did is ______________ good.

3. Sam and Matt go up and down ______________.

4. Dick and Nan ______________ the big pan.

Name ______________________________

A sentence is a group of words that tells a whole idea. Every sentence begins with a capital letter and ends with a special mark.

Write each sentence correctly.
Begin with a capital letter.
Add the end mark shown in ( ).

1. she can use my help (period)

____

2. where did it land (question mark)

____

3. look at it go up (exclamation mark)

____

4. the wind will help now (period)

____

CA LC 1.6 Use knowledge of the basic rules of punctuation and capitalization when writing.

Name ____________________________________

A B C D E F G H I J K L M N O P Q R S T U V W X Y Z

The first letter of a word tells you where to put it in ABC order.

Read each set of words. Circle the word that comes last in ABC order.

1.	miss	kick	ran	
2.	pass	go	hit	
3.	jump	over	run	fast
4.	land	use	miss	go
5.	pass	land	hit	over

Name ____________________

A. Add a part from the box to make a spelling word. Circle the picture that matches the word.

nd	st	nk	lp

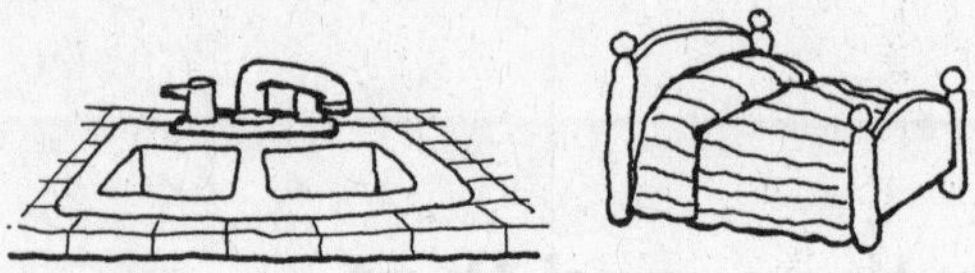

1. si ____________

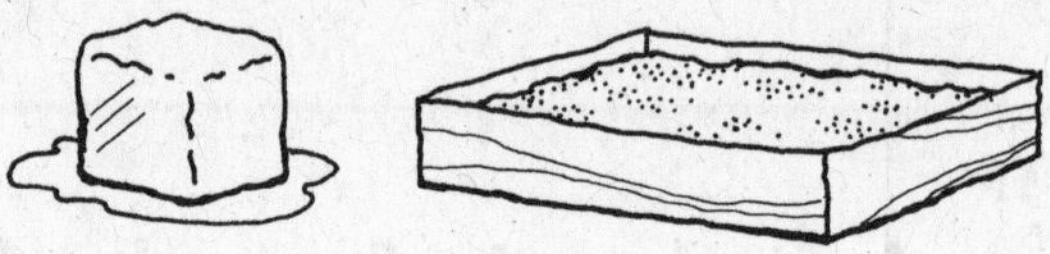

2. sa ____________

3. fa ____________

4. la ____________

B. Circle the word that is correct.

5. filp flip flipp

6. black balck

7. snig sinng sing

8. verry very

CA LC 1.8 Spell three- and four-letter short-vowel words and grade-level-appropriate sight words correctly.

Name ______________________________

As you read Soccer, fill in the Author's Purpose Chart.

Clue

Clue

Author's Purpose

How does the Author's Purpose Chart help you understand the story Soccer?

Name ______________________________

Some authors write to tell a story. Some authors write to tell about real people or things.

Read the sentences. Choose the author's purpose.

1. Ben the cat likes to play with a pink ball. Look at Ben run! Look at Ben go!
   - ○ tell a story
   - ○ tell about real people or things

2. An ant can walk. A shark can swim. A cat can run. A kangaroo can hop.
   - ○ tell a story
   - ○ tell about real people or things

3. Where is the band? The band is not here! "What will we do now?" said Crab. "We will play!" said Ant.
   - ○ tell a story
   - ○ tell about real people or things

4. Dogs can jump up and down. Dogs can sit. Dogs can run fast. Dogs can play with you.
   - ○ tell a story
   - ○ tell about real people or things

Name ____________________

Write C if a sentence is correct. If a sentence is not correct, write the letter or letters to tell how you would make it right.

Ⓐ Begin with a capital letter.
Ⓑ Put a special mark at the end.
Ⓒ Do not change.

1. rick jumps on the mat. ____________

2. Will Pam run fast ____________

3. she can go like the wind ____________

4. Now Sam runs and jumps. ____________

5. did he land in the sand? ____________

6. That was a very good jump! ____________

Go back to the sentences. Circle any letter that should be capital. Put the correct mark at the end.

CA LC 1.6 Use knowledge of the basic rules of punctuation and capitalization when writing.

Name ______________________________

Practice

Fluency: Choral Read: Phrasing

As I read, I will pay attention to pauses for sentence punctuation.

What can be in a hill of sand?
08 Little, black ants! The ants have a plan.
16 The ants can dig in the sand.
23 Little ants can help, too.
28 Little ants dig down in the sand.
35 Ants do not slip down in the sand.
43 Ants can dig very, very fast. 49

Comprehension Check

1. Where do the ants live?
2. What can the ants do?

	Words Read	–	Number of Errors	=	Words Correct Score
First Read		–		=	
Second Read		–		=	

R 1.16 Read aloud with fluency in a manner that sounds like natural speech.

Name ________________________________

Words in a poem often **rhyme.** Rhyming words begin with different sounds and end with the same sound.

map **tap**

Read the poem. Write the rhyming words on the line. Circle the same sound in each word.

Where Did the Ball Go?

1. Pam can kick.
Now she is very quick.

____

2. Where will the ball land?
Will it sink in the sand?

____

3. Now it will fall.
It is just a red ball.

____

Name ______________________________

The letter **o** stands for the middle sound in **log**.

Blend the sounds and say the word. Then write the word and circle the picture.

1. p o t ____________

2. h o g ____________

3. b o x ____________

4. t o p ____________

5. f o x ____________

Name ______________________________

hop	top	log	hog	hot
lot	fast	sing	our	they

Circle the words that have the short o sound.

Write the words you circled.

1. ____________ **2.** ____________ **3.** ____________

4. ____________ **5.** ____________ **6.** ____________

CA LC 1.8 Spell three- and four-letter short-vowel words and grade-level-appropriate sight words correctly.

Name ________________________________

Write the word that completes each sentence.

Our	two	her	They

1. __________ cat is a mom.

2. The small cat naps with __________ mom.

3. This mom has __________ dogs.

4. __________ play with mom.

CA R 1.11 Read common, irregular sight words (e.g., *the, have, said, come, give, of*).

Name ______________________________________

A noun is a word that names a person, a place, or a thing.

Say the name of the noun in the picture.

person place thing

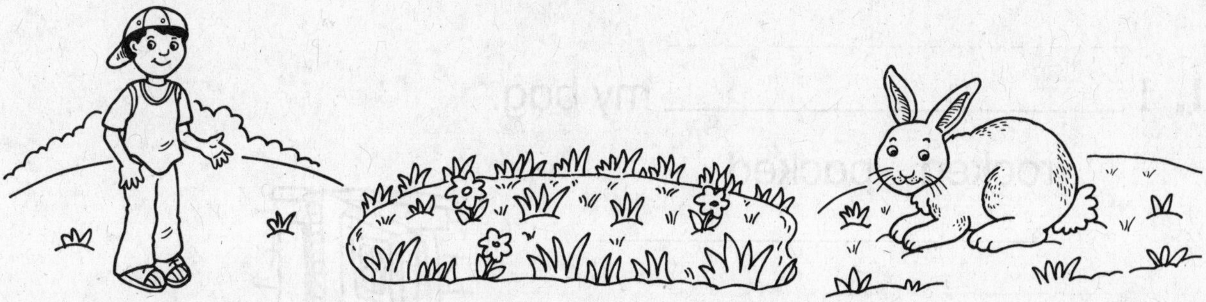

Circle the noun in each sentence.

1. Look at the little dog.

2. It sits in the grass.

3. The mom runs over.

4. They see an ant.

5. It digs up sand.

6. What a big hill that is!

CA LC 1.2 Identify and correctly use singular and plural nouns.

Name ______________________________

You can add **-ed** to some action words to tell what someone or something did. **walk + ed = walked**

Circle the word that completes the sentence. Then write the word.

1. I ______________________ my bag.

   rocked   packed

2. Dad ______________________ the  .

   locked   packed

3. Bob ______________________ up the dog.

   picked   licked

4. The cat ______________________ up on my lap.

   jumped   picked

5. Pat ______________________ the  .

   rocked   kicked

CA **R 1.14** Read inflectional forms (e.g., *-s*, *-ed*, *-ing*) and root words (e.g., *look*, *looked*, *looking*).

Name ______________________________

Look at each set of words.
One word in each set is spelled correctly.
Use a pencil to fill in the circle in front of that word.
Sample A is done for you.

Sample A:

- ○ A. fassed
- ● B. fast
- ○ C. fasd

1. ○ A. lot
○ B. lott
○ C. lat

2. ○ A. hoog
○ B. hig
○ C. hog

3. ○ A. hopp
○ B. hap
○ C. hop

4. ○ A. ttop
○ B. toop
○ C. top

5. ○ A. hot
○ B. hott
○ C. hoht

6. ○ A. loog
○ B. log
○ C. logg

CA **LC 1.8** Spell three- and four-letter short-vowel words and grade-level-appropriate sight words correctly.

Name ______________________________

As you read Animal Moms and Dads, fill in the Main Idea and Details Web.

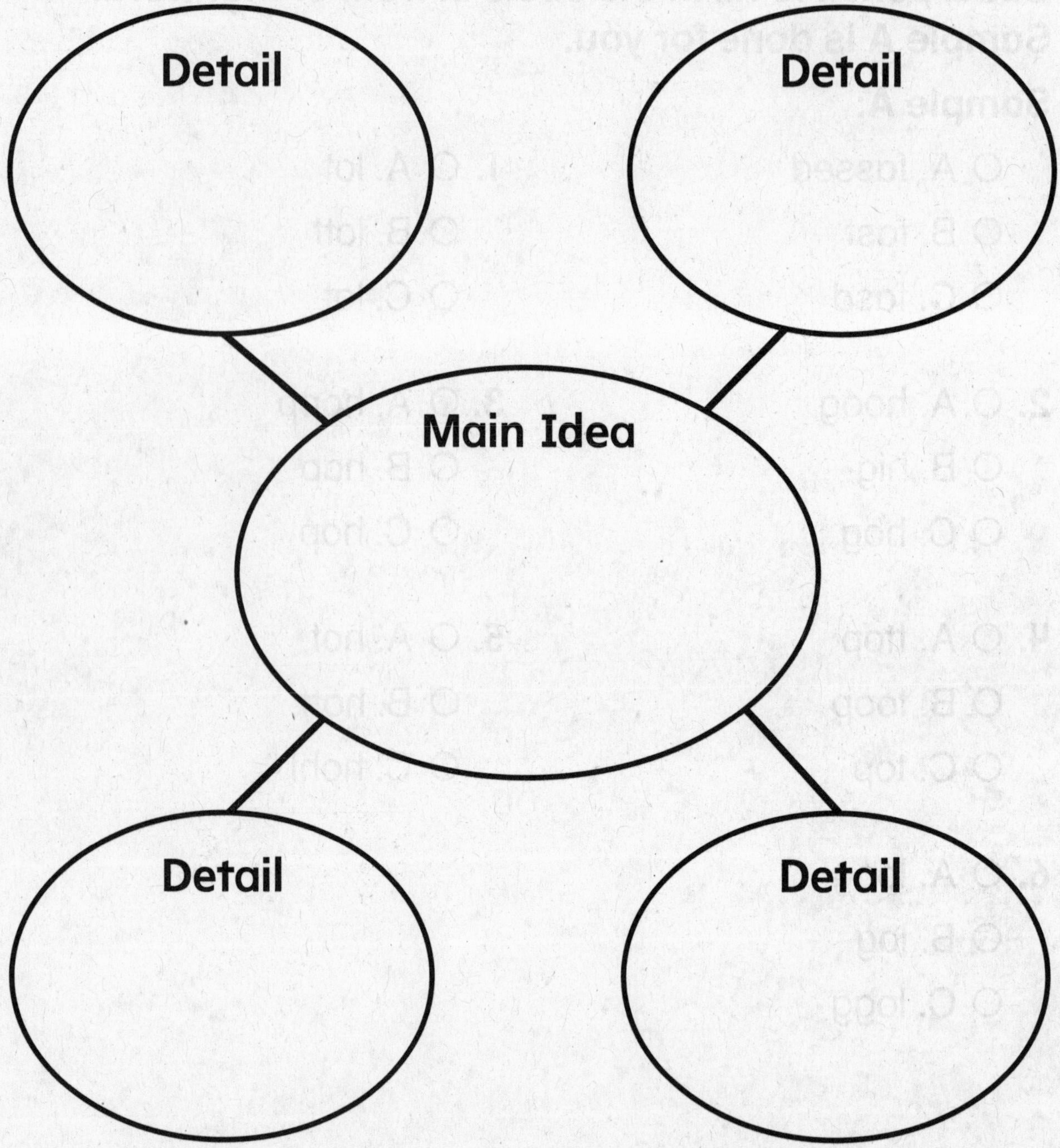

How does the Main Idea and Details Web help you retell Animal Moms and Dads?

Name ______________________________

Look at the picture. Circle all the sentences that tell about the picture.

1. The children are eating lunch.
2. Kim and Bob play ball.
3. The children go to school.
4. Pam and Jack climb.
5. The children like to jump rope.
6. The dog wants to play, too.

Write a sentence that tells the main idea of the picture.

____

____

Name ________________________________

A noun names a person, place, or thing.

Most sentences contain nouns.

Begin every sentence with a capital letter.

End every statement with a period.

Write the statement correctly. Circle the nouns.

1. i see one little cat

2. it can not go over the log

3. a cat does not jump like a frog

4. the mom will help

CA LC 1.2 Identify and correctly use singular and plural nouns.

Name ____________________

As I read, I will pay attention to patterns in the story.

Our dog is Bob. What can a dog do?
09 Bob can flop down on a mat and nap.
18 Our cat is Miss Spot. What can a cat do?
28 Miss Spot can sit and lick her paws.
36 Our two pets are Bob and Miss Spot.
44 What can they do?
48 Miss Spot can hiss at Bob the dog! 56

Comprehension Check

1. What can Bob do?

2. What can Miss Spot do?

	Words Read	–	Number of Errors	=	Words Correct Score
First Read		–		=	
Second Read		–		=	

CA **R 1.16** Read aloud with fluency in a manner that sounds like natural speech.

Name ____________________

Rhythmic patterns are sounds and words that repeat to give a poem a beat.

Read the poem.

One little cat,
Sat on a mat.
She did not run,
She did not pat.

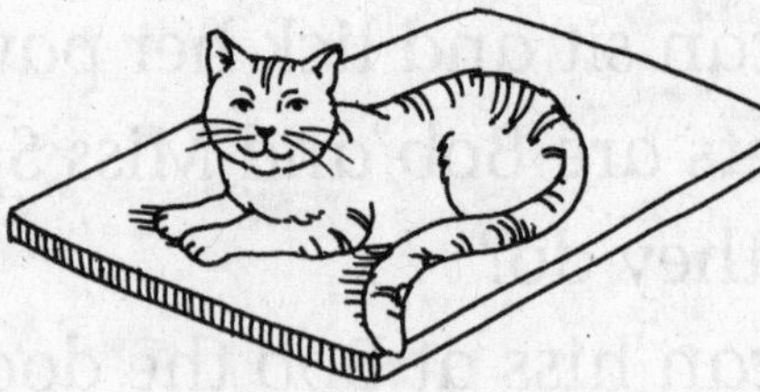

One little frog,
Sat on a log.
He did not jump,
He did not jog.

1. Write three words that rhyme in the first verse.

______________ ______________ ______________

2. Write three words that rhyme in the second verse.

______________ ______________ ______________

3. Underline three words that repeat in the first verse.
4. Underline three words that repeat in the second verse.

Name ______________________

Use the words from the box to name each picture.

dress	net	cent	leg	bed	ten

1.  ______________

2.  ______________

3. 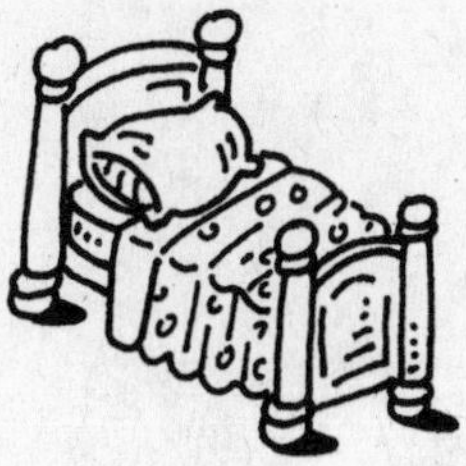 ______________

4.  ______________

5. 10 ______________

6.  ______________

CA **R 1.4** Distinguish initial, medial, and final sounds in single-syllable words.

Name ______________________________

leg	beg	men	hen	let
get	top	lot	no	some

Complete each spelling word by writing the letter that makes the short e sound.

1. h _____ n

2. m _____ n

3. b _____ g

4. l _____ g

5. g _____ t

6. l _____ t

CA **LC 1.8** Spell three- and four-letter short-vowel words and grade-level-appropriate sight words correctly.

Name ______________________________

Practice

High-Frequency Words/Vocabulary

Write a word from the box to complete each sentence.

Who	some	of	No	eat

1. Did you get ______________  for me?

2. ______________ can get the  down?

3. The bag ______________  is in the box.

4. ______________, I can not ride a .

5. Can I ______________ with you?

CA **R 1.11** Read common, irregular sight words (e.g., *the, have, said, come, give, of*).

Name ____________________

A plural noun names more than one person, place, or thing.
Add **-s** to make most nouns plural.

Example: one **cat** two **cats**

Circle the plural noun in each sentence.

1. Mom has a lot of jobs to do.
2. The kids like to help her.
3. Pam will fix the beds.
4. The dogs have to eat now.
5. Jack does the pots in the sink.
6. Now we can have some eggs.

CA **LC 1.2** Identify and correctly use singular and plural nouns.

Name ______________________________

A **contraction** is a short form of two words. An **apostrophe (')** takes the place of the missing letters. can + not = **can't**

didn't	can't	doesn't	isn't

A. Write the contractions.

1. does not ______________________

2. did not ______________________

3. can not ______________________

4. is not ______________________

B. Write a sentence using a contraction from the box.

____

CA R 1.13 Read compound words and contractions.

Name ____________________

A. Mark an X on the line next to the word spelled correctly.

1. enm ______

nme ______

men ______

2. leg ______

elg ______

gle ______

3. get ______

teg ______

egt ______

4. pto ______

top ______

otp ______

B. Use a letter from the box to write a spelling word.

n	**b**	**t**	**m**

5. ______ o

6. so ______ e

CA LC 1.8 Spell three- and four-letter short-vowel words and grade-level-appropriate sight words correctly.

Name ____________________________________

As you read Little Red Hen, fill in the Retelling Chart.

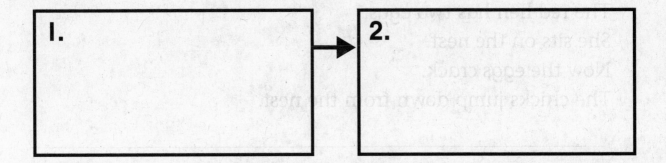

Little Red Hen	
1.	2.
3.	4.
5.	6.

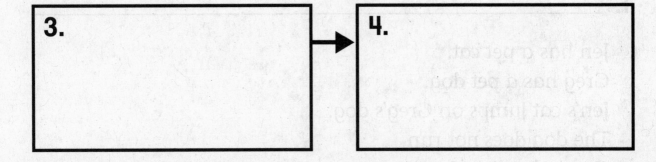

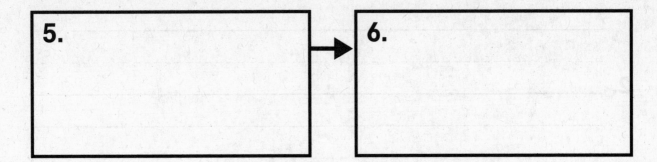

How does the Retelling Chart help you remember Little Red Hen?

CA **R 3.1** Identify and describe the elements of plot, setting, and character(s) in a story, as well as the story's beginning, middle, and ending.

Name ______________________________

When you **retell** a story, you tell only the important parts.

Read each story. Write a new sentence that tells only the important parts. Then draw a picture.

The red hen has two eggs.
She sits on the nest.
Now the eggs crack.
The chicks jump down from the nest.

____

1. ______________________________

Jen has a pet cat.
Greg has a pet dog.
Jen's cat jumps on Greg's dog.
The dog does not run.
Greg's dog licks Jen's cat.

____

2. ______________________________

____

____

CA R 3.1 Identify and describe the elements of plot, setting, and character(s) in a story, as well as the story's beginning, middle, and ending.

Name ______________________________

Add **-s** or **-es** to form the plural of most nouns. Begin every sentence with a capital letter. End a question with a question mark.

Find the mistakes. Circle the letters that should be capital. Underline the nouns that should be plural. Add the correct end mark.

1. will you help me up

2. who fell on all the egg

3. the two cat jumped on me

4. where are they now

5. do you see some little leg over there

6. what is in the two bush

CA LC 1.2 Identify and correctly use singular and plural nouns.

Name ______________________________

Practice
Fluency: Echo Read: Intonation

As I read, I will pay attention to intonation in the passage.

Look at the farm. What can you get from a
10 farm?
11 Look at the cows. We get milk from the cows.
21 Who will have some of the milk?
28 Look at the hen. We get eggs from the hen.
38 Who will eat some of the eggs? 45

Comprehension Check

1. What do we get from cows?

2. What do we get from hens?

	Words Read	–	Number of Errors	=	Words Correct Score
First Read		–		=	
Second Read		–		=	

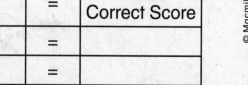

CA **R 1.16** Read aloud with fluency in a manner that sounds like natural speech.

Name ______________________________

A **diagram** is a picture that shows the parts of something.

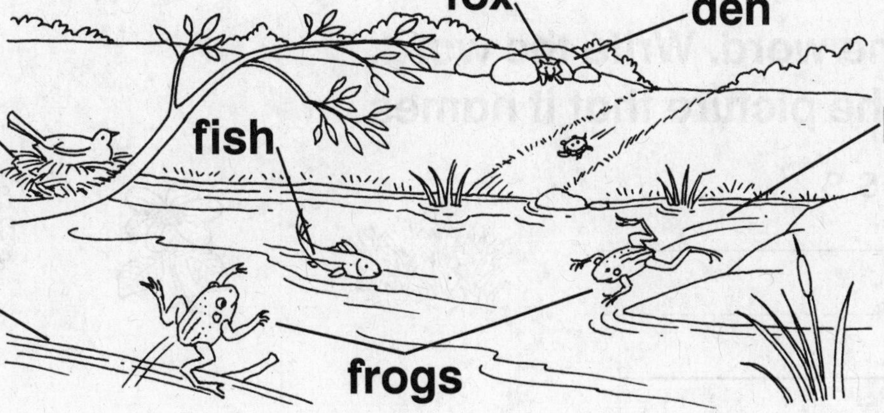

Write a word from the diagram to complete each sentence.

1. Two frogs jump in the ______________.

2. The ______________ is in the  .

3. A fox is in a ______________.

4. A ______________ is in the pond.

Name ______________________________

Sometimes consonants form a **blend**. You can hear each consonant sound in a **consonant blend**.

Read the word. Write the word.
Circle the picture that it names.

1. grass

2. track

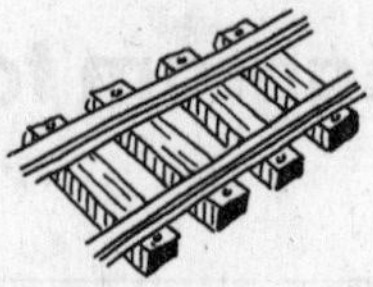

3. swing

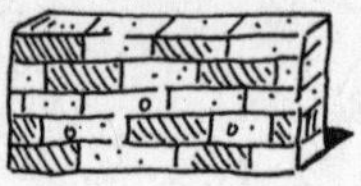

4. snap

5. crib

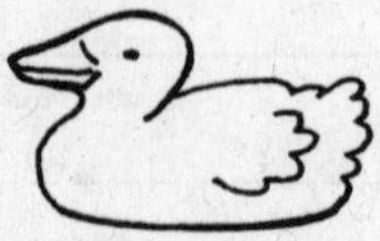

CA **R 1.10** Generate the sounds from all the letters and letter patterns, including consonant blends and long- and short-vowel patterns (i.e., phonograms), and blend those sounds into recognizable words.

Name ______________________________

spill	spin	grab	grass	trap
trip	men	let	out	many

Read each row of words. Put an X on the word that does not belong.

1. spill	spin	out
2. men	grab	let
3. trap	spill	trip
4. spin	grab	grass
5. out	let	crib
6. men	grass	many

CA **LC 1.8** Spell three- and four-letter short-vowel words and grade-level-appropriate sight words correctly.

Name ________________________________

live	many	out	place

Write the word that completes each sentence.

1. Come to our ________________.

2. We ________________ here.

3. We have ________________ pals.

4. We go ________________ to play.

CA **R 2.4** Use context to resolve ambiguities about word and sentence meanings.

Name ______________________________

Some plural nouns do not end with **-s** or **-es**. These nouns use a new word to name more than one.

A. Say the nouns and their plurals.

child children

man men

goose geese

mouse mice

foot feet

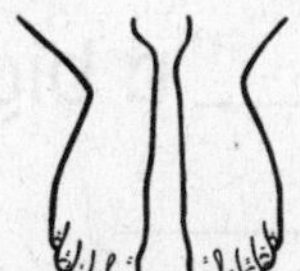

B. Circle the plural or plurals in each group.

1. mouse	man	geese
2. men	foot	child
3. goose	children	feet
4. man	child	mice

CA LC 1.2 Identify and correctly use singular and plural nouns.

Name ________________________________

You can add **-ing** to some action words.

A. Add <u>-ing</u> to the words in the box.

look ____________ jump ____________

play ____________ wash ____________

B. Complete the sentences with the words you wrote.

1. Beth is ____________ a big dog.

2. They are ____________ for a lost cat.

3. I am ____________ with a little ship.

4. We are ____________ up and down.

CA **R 1.14** Read inflectional forms (e.g., *-s*, *-ed*, *-ing*) and root words (e.g., *look*, *looked*, *looking*).

Name ______________________________

A. Circle the word in each row that is spelled correctly.

1. otu	outt	out
2. let	lett	tel
3. meny	menny	many

B. Write the spelling words that start with the consonant blend sp.

4. ______________ ______________

Write the spelling words that start with the consonant blend gr.

5. ______________ ______________

Write the spelling words that start with the consonant blend tr.

6. ______________ ______________

CA **LC 1.8** Spell three- and four-letter short-vowel words and grade-level-appropriate sight words correctly.

Name ______________________________

Practice

Comprehension: Main Idea and Details Chart

As you read On the Map!, fill in the Main Idea and Details Chart.

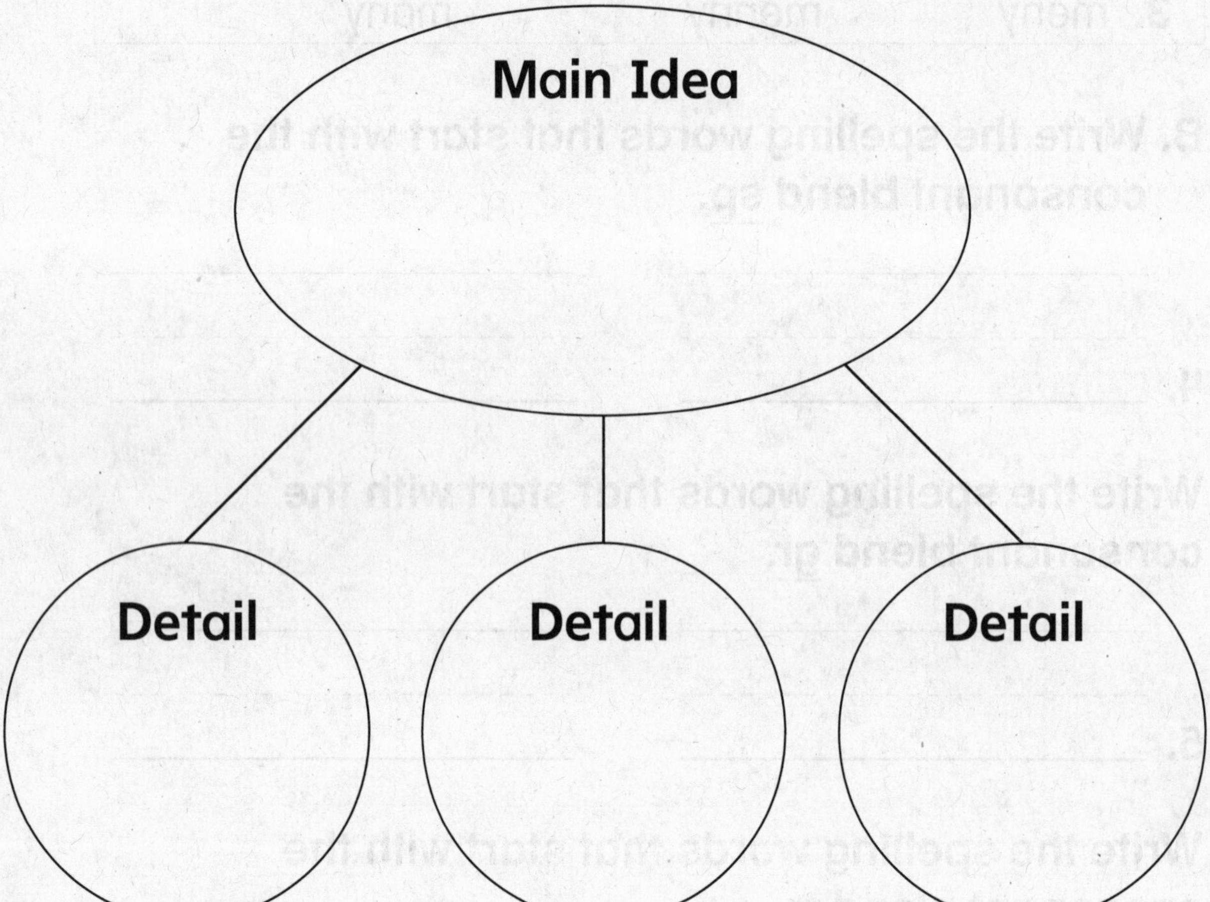

How does the information you wrote in this Main Idea and Details Chart help you retell On the Map!?

Name ______________________________

The **main idea** tells what the story is about.
The **details** tell more about the main idea.

A. Write a sentence that tells the main idea.

Frogs live in the pond.

So do fish and  .

Frogs jump in and out of the pond.

 go in and out, too.

____

B. Draw a picture to show what else lives in a pond.

Name ___________________________

Remember that some nouns use new words to name more than one. Begin every sentence with a capital letter. End an exclamation with an exclamation point.

Write C if a sentence is correct.
If a sentence is not correct, circle the mistakes.

1. Don't go in there!

2. the gooses will not like it.

3. that goose is very mad now?

4. Childs, get out quick.

5. She can peck with her bill!

CA L 1.2 Identify and correctly use singular and plural nouns.
L 1.6 Use knowledge of the basic rules of punctuation and capitalization when writing.

Name ______________________________

Practice
Fluency: Choral Read: Intonation

As I read, I will pay attention to questions in the passage.

Brad is a crab. Brad has no hands.
08 A crab has claws! What can Brad do?
16 He likes to do tricks! Brad can grab a stick.
26 What can Brad do with a stick?
33 He can drag it in the sand.
40 He can drag it back!
45 How can Brad grab a stick?
51 His claws go "Snap!" 55

Comprehension Check

1. What is Brad?

2. What can Brad do with his claws?

	Words Read	–	Number of Errors	=	Words Correct Score
First Read		–		=	
Second Read		–		=	

CA **R 1.16** Read aloud with fluency in a manner that sounds like natural speech.

Name ____________________

A **dictionary** gives the meaning of words.

grand very big

ship a big 

mend to fix

lamb a little 

A. Write a dictionary word to complete each sentence.

1. The ____________ likes to run and play.

2. The ship is very ____________.

3. I have to ____________ my pants.

4. A ____________ is too big for a pond.

B. Write a new sentence for one of the words.

5. ________________________________

Name ______________________________

The letter **u** stands for the middle sound in **bus**.

Circle the word that names each picture.
Then write the word.

1.

bun big

2.

pot pup

3.
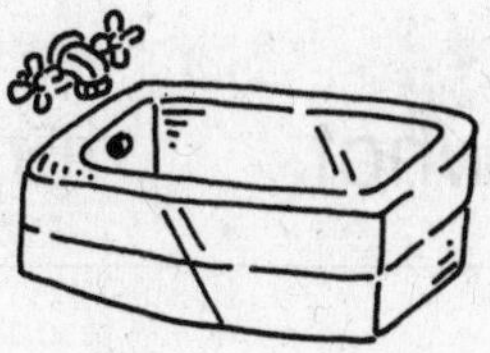
ten tub

4.

sun sad

5.
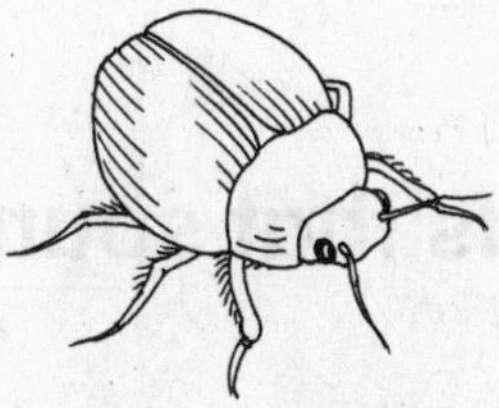
bat bug

6.

drip drum

CA R 1.4 Distinguish initial, medial, and final sounds in single-syllable words.

Name ______________________________

run	fun	nut	cut	bug
rug	grass	spin	could	one

In each row put an X on the word that does not belong. Then write the spelling word.

1. what	fun	this	____________
2. run	two	up	____________
3. bug	sit	tug	____________
4. fun	sun	man	____________

Write the spelling words that sound like hug.

5. ____________ **6.** ____________

Write the spelling words that sound like hut.

7. ____________ **8.** ____________

CA **LC 1.8** Spell three- and four-letter short-vowel words and grade-level-appropriate sight words correctly.

Name ______________________________

Write a word from the box to complete each sentence.

could	again	one	make	Then	three

1. I see ______________ huts.

2. I like the red ______________.

3. I ______________ live in it.

4. ______________ I can have two trees.

5. I will ______________ a swing in one.

6. I will use it again and ______________.

CA **R 1.11** Read common, irregular sight words (e.g., *the, have, said, come, give, of*).

Name ______________________________

A noun that names a special person or place is called a proper noun. A proper noun begins with a capital letter.

Examples: **Yan** **Jill** **Texas**

Write the proper noun in each group.

1. Rick drum play ____________

2. hum Hal he ____________

3. Lin kids fun ____________

4. show let's Jen ____________

5. Atlanta shop she ____________

Name ______________________________

A **contraction** is a short form of two words. An **apostrophe** (') takes the place of one or more letters.

he's	it's	let's	she's	that's

Read each sentence. Then write the contraction for the underlined words.

1. Mom said <u>she is</u> going with us. ______________

2. <u>That is</u> a big truck! ______________

3. <u>Let us</u> run and jump. ______________

4. Ted said <u>he is</u> playing the drum. ______________

5. <u>It is</u> a dull rug. ______________

CA R 1.13 Read compound words and contractions.

Name ______________________________

A. Change one letter to make a spelling word with the short u sound. Then write the word on the line.

1. not ______________

2. bag ______________

3. rag ______________

4. ran ______________

5. fan ______________

6. cat ______________

B. Circle the word that is spelled correctly.

7. one   oen   eonn

8. cood   couide   could

CA LC 1.8 Spell three- and four-letter short-vowel words and grade-level-appropriate sight words correctly.

Name ______________________________

As you read The Pigs, the Wolf and the Mud, fill in the Plot Chart.

Beginning

↓

Middle

↓

End

How does the Plot Chart help you better understand The Pigs, the Wolf and the Mud?

CA **R 3.1** Identify and describe the elements of plot, setting, and character(s) in a story, as well as the story's beginning, middle, and ending.

Name ______________________________

Read the story.

Who Could It Be?

Meg lives in a small home. Bill lives in a small home, too. Meg and Bill play. They are pals. They like to ride bikes. They like to dress up. They like to play ball.

Who will live in the red home? It could be a boy. It could be a girl. Meg and Bill wait. They sit and see. Then out run three! Now Meg and Bill have many pals. They can have lots of fun!

Read the sentences. Write B for the beginning sentences, M for the middle ones, and E for the end ones.

1. Meg and Bill have three pals now. ______

2. Meg and Bill live in small homes. ______

3. They sit to see who is in the red home. ______

4. Meg and Bill see three run out. ______

CA **R 3.1** Identify and describe the elements of plot, setting, and character(s) in a story, as well as the story's beginning, middle, and ending.

Name ____________________

Begin a proper noun with a capital letter. Some proper nouns are more than one word. Begin each word in a proper noun with a capital letter.

Circle the words that should have capital letters.

1. Al and pam go to the banks school.

2. miss ann has a good band there.

3. "I play the drums," said chan.

4. I got them in a shop on Tip top street.

5. The band will play in new york City.

6. Will nick sing with the band?

Name ____

As I read, I will pay attention to phrasing in the story.

Look at the big bear. Look at her cubs.
09 What can the two cubs do? They can play.
18 They can look for food to eat.
25 The cubs can rest. They take a long nap.
34 The cubs can play on the rocks. 41

Comprehension Check

1. What are cubs?
2. What can the cubs do?

	Words Read	–	Number of Errors	=	Words Correct Score
First Read		–		=	
Second Read		–		=	

CA **R 1.16** Read aloud with fluency in a manner that sounds like natural speech.

Name ____________________

Photographs are pictures that show people, animals, and things in real life.

Look at the picture.

We will have a big place to live!

Write your own sentence about the picture.

Name ______________________________

Read each word. Listen to the sounds **sh** and **th** stand for.

pa**th** **th**ink **sh**ip **sh**op di**sh** ba**th**

Use the words in the box to name each picture. Then circle the letters that stand for the sounds sh and th.

1.  ______________________

2.  ______________________

3.  ______________________

4.  ______________________

5.  ______________________

CA **R 1.10** Generate the sounds from all the letters and letter patterns, including consonant blends and long- and short-vowel patterns (i.e., phonograms), and blend those sounds into recognizable words.

Name ______________________________

fish	shop	ship	with	thin
thank	run	bug	want	all

Circle the words that have the th sound. Underline the words that have the sh sound.

Write the words you circled.

1. ______________ 2. ______________ 3. ______________

Write the words you underlined.

4. ______________ 5. ______________ 6. ______________

CA **LC 1.8** Spell three- and four-letter short-vowel words and grade-level-appropriate sight words correctly.

Name ______________________________

Write a word from the box to complete each sentence.

all	want	under	Put	show	together

1. ______________ on a hat.

2. Sit ______________ the tent.

3. Come see the ______________!

4. The kids ______________ play in a band.

5. You will ______________ to see it.

6. I like ______________ the songs they play.

CA R 1.11 Read common, irregular sight words (e.g., *the, have, said, come, give, of*).

Some proper nouns name the days of the week. Some proper nouns name the months. The names of the days and the months begin with capital letters.

Say the days. Circle the capital letters.

Monday Tuesday Wednesday

Thursday Friday Saturday Sunday

Say the months. Circle the capital letters.

January February March April

May June July August

September October November December

1. What day do you like best?

____

2. What month do you like best?

____

CA LC 1.6 Use knowledge of the basic rules of punctuation and capitalization when writing.

Name ______________________________

A **compound word** is made up of two small words.

rose + bush = **rosebush**

back + yard = **backyard**

Match a word on the left to a word on the right to make a compound word. Then write the word.

1.  bath hill ______________

2.  down one ______________

3. any care ______________

4. day robe ______________

Use a compound word in a sentence.

5. ______________________________

CA R 1.13 Read compound words and contractions.

Name ______________________________

Pick th or sh to correctly write a spelling word.

1. wi ____
2. ____ ip
3. ____ ank
4. fi ____
5. ____ op
6. ____ in

Complete each word to make a spelling word.

7. a ____ l
8. ____ ____ nt

CA **LC 1.8** Spell three- and four-letter short-vowel words and grade-level-appropriate sight words correctly.

Name ______________________________

Practice

Comprehension: Retelling Chart

As you read Beth and the Band, fill in the Retelling Chart.

Beth and the Band	
1.	→ 2.
3.	→ 4.
5.	→ 6.
7.	→ 8.

How does the Retelling Chart help you visualize what happens in Beth and the Band?

Name ______________________________

When you **retell** a story, you tell only the important parts.

Read the story. Then look at it again. Underline the sentences that retell the story.

Ben wants to use his fishing rod.
Ben sits down at the pond with his fishing rod.
Ben sits and sits.
Ben sees a frog.
Ben sees a bug.
At last Ben gets a fish!

Draw three pictures to retell the story.

Name ______________________________

Begin the names of days, months, and holidays with capital letters.

Circle the letters that should be capital. Write the day, the month, or the holiday correctly.

1. We had fun on new year's day. ______________

2. That was in january. ______________

3. Today is tuesday, February 14. ______________

4. Then it must be valentine's Day. ______________

5. On monday, we put little red flags at school.
____

6. What fun things can we do in march?
____

CA LC 1.6 Use knowledge of the basic rules of punctuation and capitalization when writing.

Name ______________________________

As I read, I will pay attention to the expression.

Tess got a dog.
04 "That is a good dog," said Tess.
11 Tess set a cup on the floor.
18 "Come and drink," said Tess.
23 Tess set a dish on the floor.
30 "Come and eat," said Tess.
35 Tess got a ball for the dog. 42

Comprehension Check

1. Why do you think Tess got a ball for the dog?

2. What things does a dog need?

	Words Read	–	Number of Errors	=	Words Correct Score
First Read		–		=	
Second Read		–		=	

CA **R 1.16** Read aloud with fluency in a manner that sounds like natural speech.

Name ______________________________

Practice

Text Feature: Directions

Directions are the steps that you follow to make or do something.

Make a Fun Box.

1. Get an egg carton.

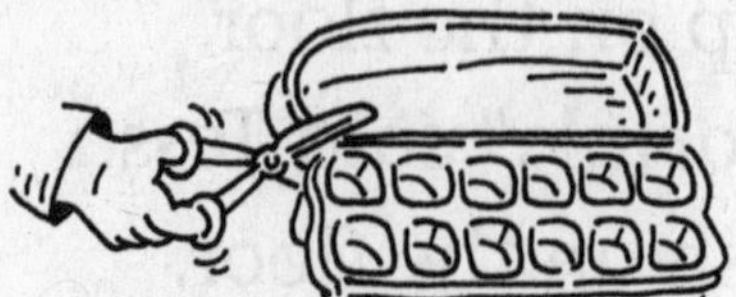

2. Cut the top.

3. Give it a fun look.

4. Put in stuff.

1. What will you make? ______________________________

2. What will you use? ______________________________

3. What will you do with the top? ______________________________

4. What will you do last? ______________________________

Name ______________________

Look at the word **gate**. The letters **a** and **e** stand for the **long a** sound you hear.

g**a**t**e**

Circle the word that names the picture. Write the word on the line.

1. 

cap cape

____

2. 

tape tap

____

3. 

pane pan

____

4. 

man mane

____

5. 

rat rate

____

6. 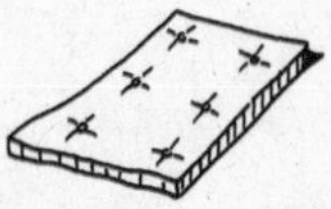

mate mat

____

CA R 1.4 Distinguish initial, medial, and final sounds in single-syllable words.

Name ______________________________

make	take	came	game	gate
late	shop	with	why	school

Read each row of words. Put an X on the word that does not belong.

1. make	shop	take
2. with	game	came
3. gate	late	why
4. crib	shop	ship
5. hop	bath	with
6. school	away	fool

CA LC 1.8 Spell three- and four-letter short-vowel words and grade-level-appropriate sight words correctly.

Name ______________________________

Read each sentence. Write a word from the box to complete the sentence.

away	school	today	way	Why

1. ______________ did the bus go in the mud?

2. This is the ______________ to play.

3. We put the blocks ______________.

4. I have to go to ______________ now.

5. We can not play ______________.

CA **R 1.11** Read common, irregular sight words (e.g., *the, have, said, come, give, of*).

Name ______________________________

A verb is a word that shows action.

Examples: Jake **jumps**. Fran **runs**.

→ **verb** ←

Find the verb in each group. Fill in the circle. The first one is done for you.

1. ○ today
   ● ride
   ○ all

2. ○ walk
   ○ oh
   ○ three

3. ○ man
   ○ make
   ○ it

4. ○ who
   ○ some
   ○ eat

5. ○ not
   ○ play
   ○ on

6. ○ go
   ○ of
   ○ many

7. ○ pull
   ○ very
   ○ good

8. ○ now
   ○ help
   ○ me

Name ______________________________

Look at the word: **wave**

Notice that the **e** is dropped when adding **-ing** or **-ed**.

wav**e** + **ing** = wav**ing** wav**e** + **ed** = wav**ed**

Add -ing to the words. Write the new word.

1. fake ______________________

2. rake ______________________

Add -ed to the words. Write the new word.

3. bake ______________________

4. fade ______________________

5. wade ______________________

CA **R 1.14** Read inflectional forms (e.g., *-s*, *-ed*, *-ing*) and root words (e.g., *look*, *looked*, *looking*).

Name ________________________________

Circle the word in each row that is spelled correctly.

1. ywh	why	wyh
2. shop	sohp	pohs
3. wiht	thiw	with
4. school	scoohl	slooch

Write the spelling words that rhyme with cake.

5. ________________ ________________

Write the spelling words that rhyme with same.

6. ________________ ________________

Write the spelling words that rhyme with ate.

7. ________________ ________________

CA LC 1.8 Spell three- and four-letter short-vowel words and grade-level-appropriate sight words correctly.

Name ______________________________

As you read On My Way to School, fill in the Retelling Chart.

1.
↓
2.
↓
3.
↓
4.

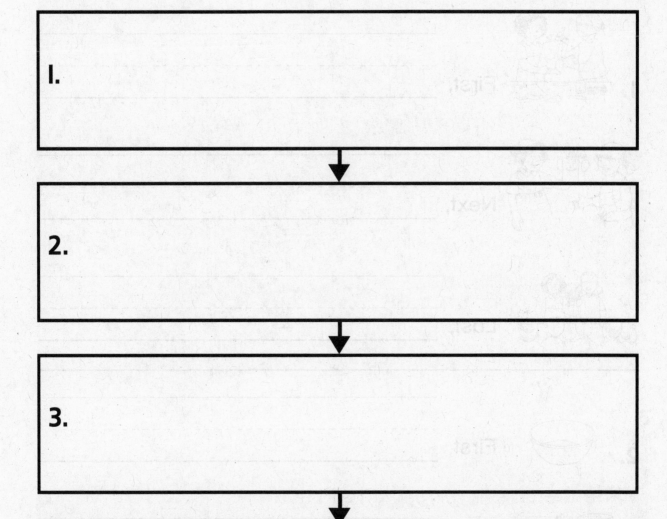

How does the Retelling Chart help you visualize what happens in On My Way to School?

CA **R 3.1** Identify and describe the elements of plot, setting, and character(s) in a story, as well as the story's beginning, middle, and ending.

Name ______________________

Practice

Comprehension: Retell

Look at the pictures. Write what happens in each picture.

1.  First, ______________________

 Next, ______________________

 Last, ______________________

2. 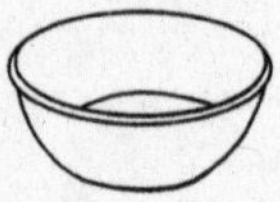 First, ______________________

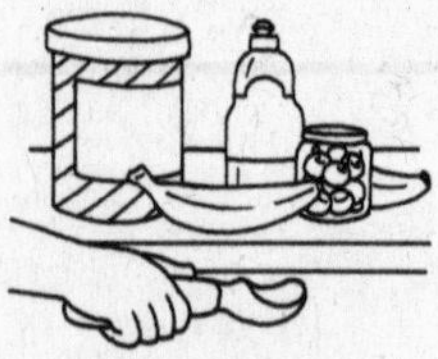 Next, ______________________

 Last, ______________________

CA **R 3.1** Identify and describe the elements of plot, setting, and character(s) in a story, as well as the story's beginning, middle, and ending.

Name ______________________________

Use verbs to show action.
Put commas after the greeting and the closing in a letter.

This letter is missing two commas and three verbs. Add the verbs from the box. Add the commas.

saved	baked	ate

Hello Nan

Mom and I ________ a cake. Then we ________ some. It was very good. I ________ some for you in a tin. Come to see me. Then you can have some cake, too.

Your best pal

Pam

Name ______________________________

As I read, I will pay attention to the intonation.

Nate sat up. He looked at the clock.
08 “Oh no! I will be late for school!”
16 Nate got dressed. He got his books. He got
25 his lunch. He put them in his backpack.
33 Nate ran down the street very fast! On the way,
43 he saw Bob. 46

Comprehension Check

1. What is the problem?

2. What does Nate do to get ready for school?

	Words Read	–	Number of Errors	=	Words Correct Score
First Read		–		=	
Second Read		–		=	

CA R 1.16 Read aloud with fluency in a manner that sounds like natural speech.

Name ______________________

A **sign** uses words or pictures to tell you what to do.

Circle the word that completes each sentence.

1. When you see 

, you _____.

stop go

2. When you see , you _____.

stop go

3. To play on the _____, we go to the .

beds swings

4. We _____ in the .

run eat

Color the traffic light with red, yellow, and green.
Put a ✔ next to the color that tells you to go.
Put an X next to the color that tells you to stop.

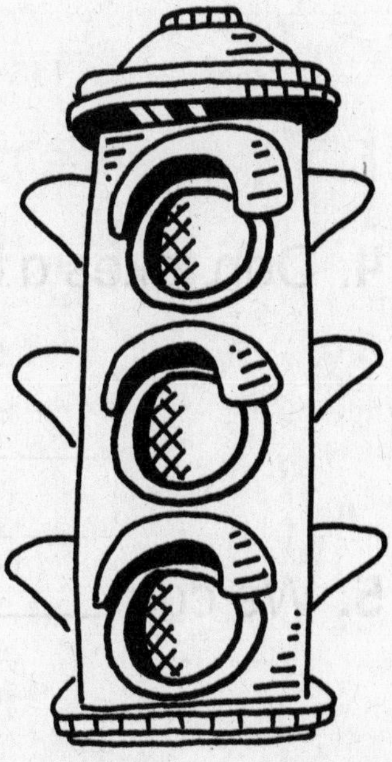

Name ______________________________

Use the words in the box to complete the sentences.

hike	hive	line	bite	bike

1. Matt races very fast on his __________.

2. What will I find in the __________?

3. We must all walk in a __________.

4. Dan takes a big __________ of his cake.

5. We can __________ up this hill.

CA R 1.4 Distinguish initial, medial, and final sounds in single-syllable words.

Name ______________________________

like	spike	ride	hide	bike
mine	make	came	how	there

Circle the words that have the long i sound.

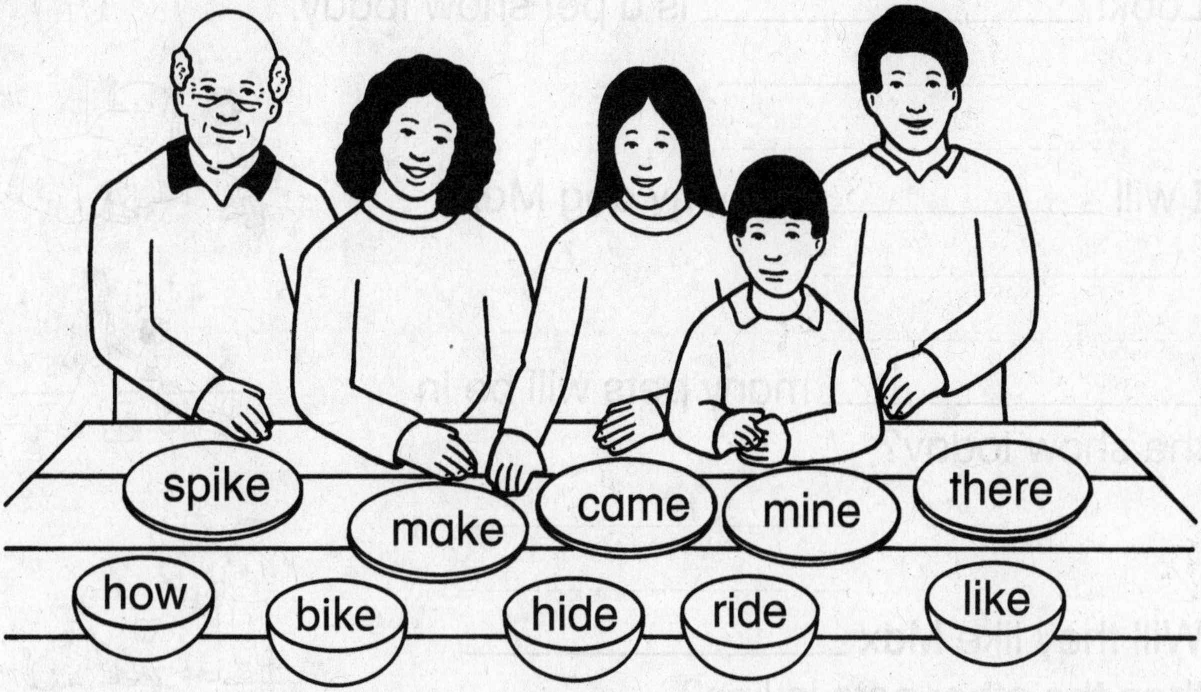

Write the words you circled.

1. ____________ 2. ____________ 3. ____________

4. ____________ 5. ____________ 6. ____________

CA **LC 1.8** Spell three- and four-letter short-vowel words and grade-level-appropriate sight words correctly.

Name ________________________________

Practice

High-Frequency Words/Vocabulary

Use the words from the box to complete the story.

call	How	more	funny	There	so

Look! ____________________ is a pet show today.

I will ____________________ my dog Max.

____________________ many pets will be in the show today?

Will they like Max ____________________ than the other pets in line?

We like to watch some of the ____________________ dogs and cats.

My Max is ____________________ good!

CA **R 1.11** Read common, irregular sight words (*e.g., the, have, said, come, give, of*).

Name ____________________

The tense of a verb tells when an action happens.

Present tense verbs tell about action that happens now.

Examples: Dell **makes** a cake. Pam **helps.**

Circle the verbs in the present tense.
Write them on the lines below.

1. The little boy trips on the rug.

2. He drops his box.

3. The blocks spilled out.

4. Ann rushed over.

5. She puts them back in the box.

________________ ________________ ________________

Name ________________________

Practice

Structural Analysis: Soft Consonants *c* and *g*

The c in **cent** stands for the **/s/** sound. This is **soft c**.
The g in **gem** stands for the **/j/** sound. This is **soft g**.

Choose a word from the box to complete each sentence. Write it on the line. Then circle each word that has the soft c sound.

race	fence	page	cage
age	nice	stage	ice

1. What ________________ are we on?
2. It is so ________________ of you to help.
3. My pet mice are out of the ________________!
4. I want to win the ________________.
5. We will stand on the ________________ to sing.
6. My water needs some ________________.

Name ____________________

Circle the spelling word in each row. Then write the spelling word.

1.	jump	how	yell	______
2.	bike	sled	crab	______
3.	want	flip	like	______
4.	there	now	here	______
5.	good	ours	mine	______
6.	hide	flip	show	______
7.	walk	ride	tap	______
8.	pin	block	spike	______

CA **LC 1.8** Spell three- and four-letter short-vowel words and grade-level-appropriate sight words correctly.

Name ______________________________

As you read Smile, Mike!, fill in the Predictions Chart.

What I Predict	What Happens

How does the Predictions Chart help you understand what happens in Smile, Mike!?

CA **R 2.5** Confirm predictions about what will happen next in a text by identifying key words (i.e., signpost words).

Name ______________________________

Read the sentences. Write the words that tell what happens next.

1. Tim's kite is ripped. Dad can fix Tim's kite.

Tim will ______________________.

2. Kim must wash her dog. Kim's dog is very big.

Mike will ______________________.

3. Sam wants to skate. Dad takes Sam to the rink.

Sam and Dad will ______________________.

4. Sam wants a nice pup. Mom and Sam go to see the pups.

Mom and Sam will ______________________.

CA **R 2.5** Confirm predictions about what will happen next in a text by identifying key words (i.e., signpost words).

Name ______________________________

Write C if a sentence is correct. If a sentence is not correct, write the letter or letters to tell how you would make it right.

Ⓐ Add **-s** to make present tense verb.

Ⓑ Capitalize a letter.

Ⓒ Do not change.

1. He looks at the book. ________

2. She pick up the dishes. ________

3. He dig up the land for Mom. ________

4. the boy take care of the hens. ________

5. He gets the eggs. ________

Name ______________________________

As I read, I will pay attention to the expression.

Meg, Jim, and Dan sat under a big branch.
09 Dan's little sister sat under the big branch, too.
18 Jim asked,
20 "What do you want to do?"
26 Meg said, "I want to put on a show. Do you
37 want to help me?"
41 Jim and Dan said, "Yes!" 46

Comprehension Check

1. Where are the children sitting?

2. What do the children want to do?

	Words Read	–	Number of Errors	=	Words Correct Score
First Read		–		=	
Second Read		–		=	

CA **R 1.16** Read aloud with fluency in a manner that sounds like natural speech.

Name ______________________________

Read the chart.

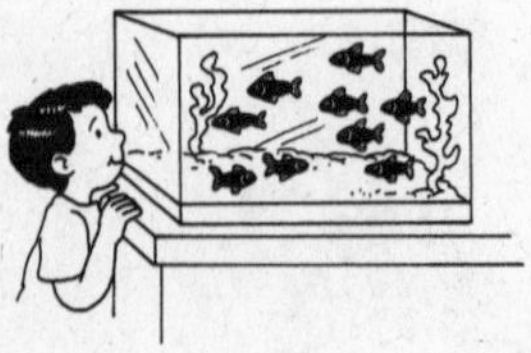

Tim's Pets	Nan's Pets
cats |||	cat	
mice 𝍸	mice ||
dog		dogs ||
fish 𝍸 ||||	fish 𝍸 𝍸

Count the pets and then complete the sentences.

1. Tim has ______________ fish.

2. Nan has ______________ mice.

3. Tim has ______________ dog.

4. Nan has ______________ fish.

Name ______________________

The letters **ch** and **tch** stand for the sounds you hear in **ch**in and dit**ch**.

The letters **wh** stand for the sound you hear in **wh**en.

Choose from the letters ch, tch, and wh to complete each word. Write the letters on the line.

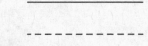

1. ________ ase

2. ________ ale

3. ca ________

4. lun ________

CA R 1.4 Distinguish initial, medial, and final sounds in single-syllable words.

Name ________________________________

Practice

Spelling: Digraphs: *ch, tch, wh*

whip	whale	catch	match	chin
chop	like	ride	from	your

Write the words that begin with ch.

1. ______________ 2. ______________

Write the words that begin with wh.

3. ______________ 4. ______________

Write the words that end with tch.

5. ______________ 6. ______________

CA **LC 1.8** Spell three- and four-letter short-vowel words and grade-level-appropriate sight words correctly.

Name ______________________________

Match each sentence to the picture that it explains.

1. Is this **your** brush? **a.** 

2. Put the dolls **into** the box. **b.** 

3. The **people** sing the song. **c.** 

4. We will make a kite **soon**. **d.** 

5. **Every** sock has dots. **e.** 

6. The gift is **from** Mom. **f.** 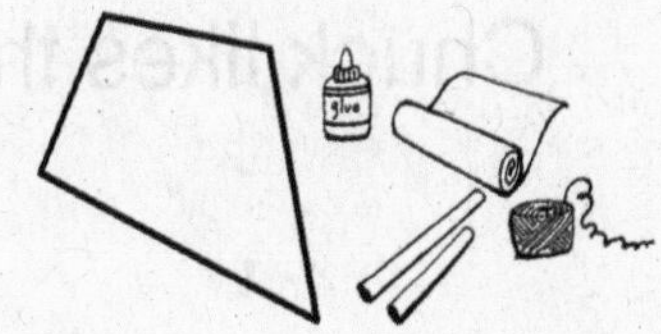

CA **R 1.11** Read common, irregular sight words (e.g., *the, have, said, come, give, of*).

Name ______________________________

A past-tense verb tells about action that happened in the past.

Examples: The sun **set**.

The boys **washed** up.

Then they **jumped** into bed.

Put a check next to the sentence that tells about the past. Circle the past-tense verb.

1. Sam made a shape with his hands.

   Sam makes a shape with his hands.

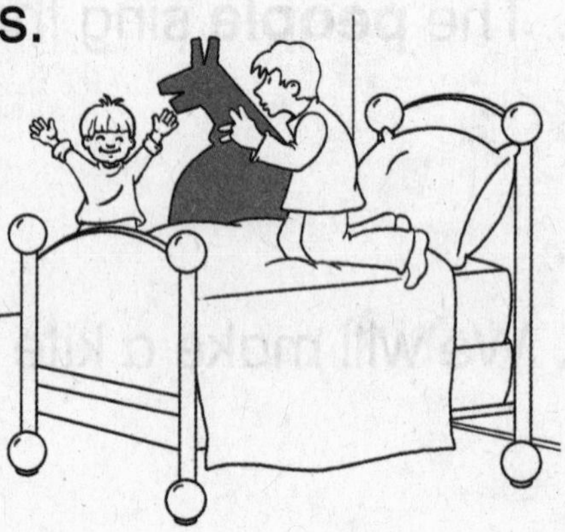

2. Chuck watches him

   Chuck watched him.

3. Sam shows Chuck a dog shape.

   Sam showed Chuck a dog shape.

4. Chuck liked that one best.

   Chuck likes that one best.

CA LC 1.0 Written and Oral English Language Conventions

Name ______________________________

You can add **-s** or **-es** to name more than one person or thing.

Circle the word in each group that names more than one. Write it on the line.

1. watch watches what ______________
2. inches pitch inch ______________
3. such lunch lunches ______________
4. catch patches patch ______________
5. kisses miss kiss ______________
6. less dresses dress ______________

Name ______________________

Practice

Spelling: Digraphs: *ch, tch, wh*

Look at each set of words.
One word in each set is spelled correctly.
Use a pencil to fill in the circle in front of that word.

1. ○ cach
   ○ cacth
   ○ catch

2. ○ chopp
   ○ cthop
   ○ chop

3. ○ cin
   ○ chin
   ○ chinn

4. ○ whale
   ○ wael
   ○ whall

5. ○ whipe
   ○ whip
   ○ wiph

6. ○ yor
   ○ yur
   ○ your

7. ○ from
   ○ fromm
   ○ fomr

8. ○ mathc
   ○ match
   ○ macht

CA **LC 1.8** Spell three- and four-letter short-vowel words and grade-level-appropriate sight words correctly.

As you read Masks! Masks! Masks!, fill in the Main Idea and Details Chart.

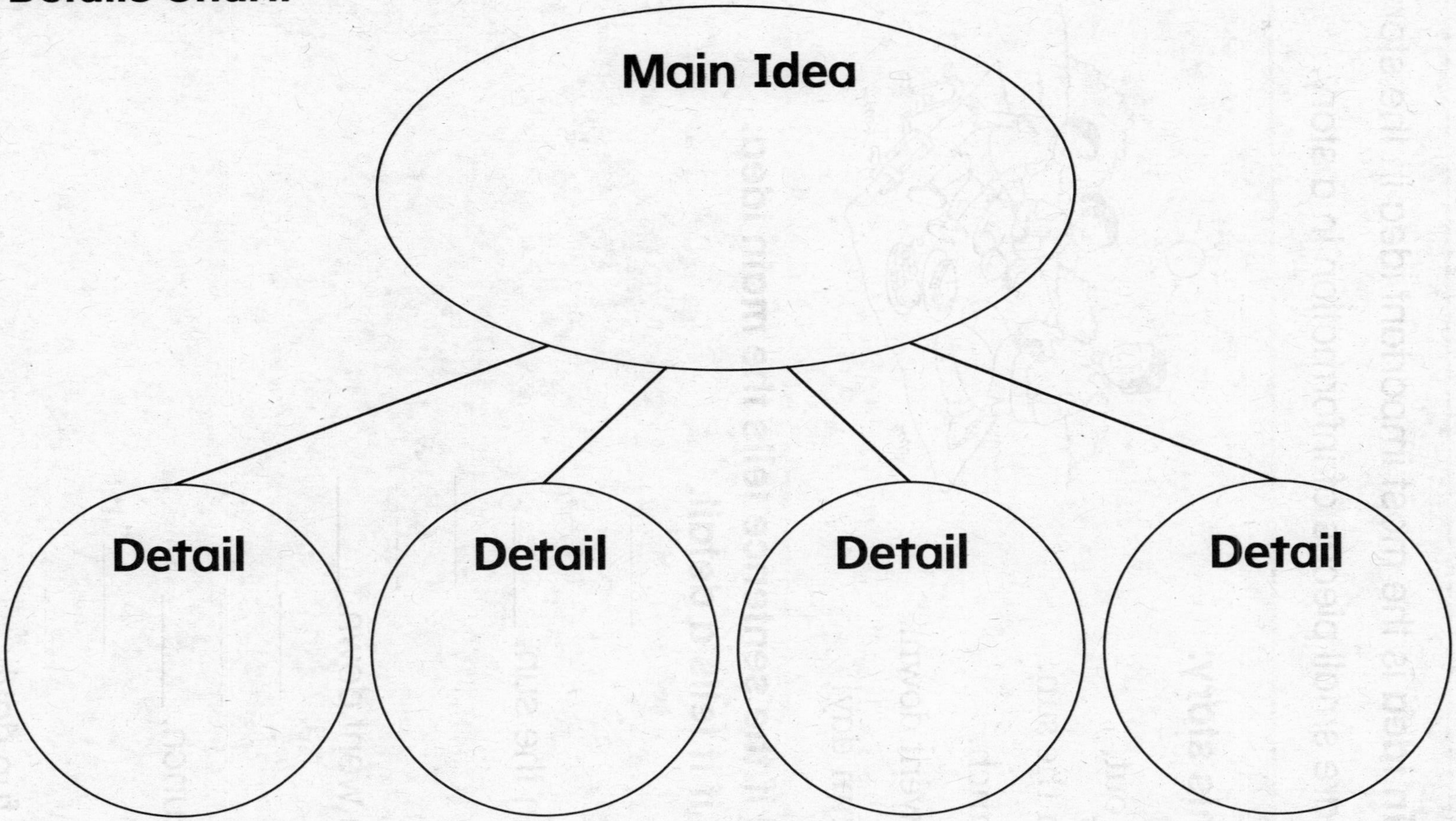

How does the information you wrote in this Main Idea and Details Chart help you retell Masks! Masks! Masks!?

Name ______________________________

The **main idea** is the most important idea in the story.

Details are small pieces of information in a story.

A. Read this story.

We went out.

We sat in the sun.

We ate lunch.

The sun went down.

It was a fun day!

B. Write M if the sentence tells the main idea. Write D if it tells a detail.

1. We sat in the sun. ______

2. The sun went down. ______

3. We ate lunch. ______

4. It was a fun day! ______

Name ______________________________

Read the story. Circle the letters that should be capital letters. Underline four verbs that should be past tense. Write the verbs in the past tense on the lines below.

Dad and james went for a walk. They walk past fitch lane. Miss chin yell hello to them. They wave to her. The sun was going down. James look back. "I can see my shadow!" he said.

1. ______________ **2.** ______________

3. ______________ **4.** ______________

Name ____________________

Practice

Fluency: Choral Read: Intonation

As I read, I will pay attention to the dialogue.

I did not want to play with Sam. So, I went to
12 see Mom and Dad.
16 "Mom," I said. "How can I play? Sam will
25 not stop. He does just what I do."
33 "He's just a little kid," Mom said.
40 "He's just little," Dad said.
45 I said, "So, can he play with you?"
53 "He can," they said. 57

Comprehension Check

1. What does Sam like to do?

2. How do Mom and Dad try to help?

	Words Read	–	Number of Errors	=	Words Correct Score
First Read		–		=	
Second Read		–		=	

CA **R 1.16** Read aloud with fluency in a manner that sounds like natural speech.

The **title** of a magazine is on the cover.
There are **articles** inside the magazine.

Use the magazine cover and article to answer the questions.

1. What is the title of the magazine?

____

2. What is on the cover?

____

3. What is the title of the article?

____

4. What could the article be about?

____

Name ____

Look at the pictures.

The letters **o_e** stand for the middle sound in **rope**.

The letters **u_e** stand for the middle sound in **cube**.

Read the word. Circle the picture that it names.

1. note

2. flute

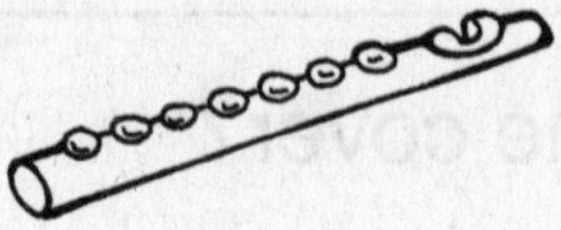
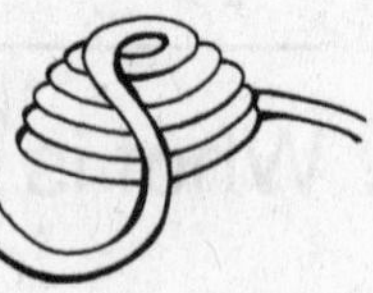

3. bone

4. **Write a sentence using some of the words.**

____

____

CA **R 1.10** Generate the sounds from all the letters and letter patterns, including consonant blends and long- and short-vowel patterns (i.e., phonograms), and blend those sounds into recognizable words.

Name ____

joke	nose	note	woke	cute
cube	chop	whale	old	new

Read each row of words. Put an X on the word that does not belong.

1. cube	cute	new
2. joke	woke	match
3. chop	note	nose
4. whale	all	whip
5. few	chin	new
6. nose	which	joke

CA **LC 1.8** Spell three- and four-letter short-vowel words and grade-level-appropriate sight words correctly.

A. Write the word that completes each sentence.

find	after	old	new

1. Dad has ______________ socks for Kim because hers are ______________.

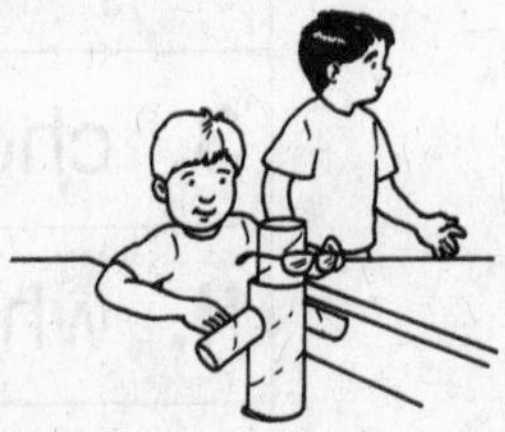

2. Can you help me ______________ my glasses?

3. We go to the park ______________ school.

B. Match the word to its meaning.

4. done — to do a job

5. work — finished

CA **R 1.11** Read common, irregular sight words (e.g., *the, have, said, come, give, of*).

Name ______________________________

The verbs **is** and **are** tell about the present.

Is tells about one person, place, or thing.

Are tells about more than one person, place, or thing.

Examples: Dad **is** there.

The cats **are** here.

Circle the verb in each sentence. Write 1 if the verb tells about one. Write 2 if the verb tells about more than one.

1. Mom is out back. ____

2. Our two dogs are with her. ____

3. The twins are in the water. ____

4. Mom is on a chair. ____

5. This game is so much fun! ____

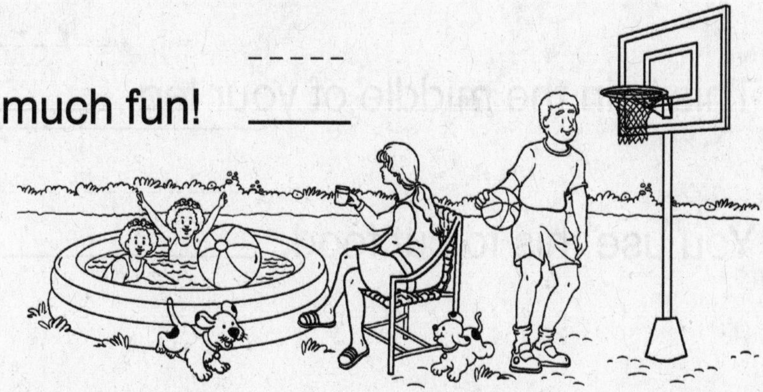

Name ______________________________

In some words, the letter ***k***, ***g***, or ***w*** is silent.

Mary **k**nits. Bob reads the si**g**n.

Write the word from the box that fits each clue. Then circle the silent letter in each word.

wren	gnat	knee	knapsack
gnaw	write	knife	wrist

1. This is a kind of bug. ______________
2. This body part is near your hand. ______________
3. This is also called a backpack. ______________
4. You do this with a pencil. ______________
5. This is in the middle of your leg. ______________
6. You use this to cut food. ______________

Name ______________________________

Circle the word in each row that is spelled correctly.

1.	nos	nose	nsoe
2.	chop	hcop	hcpo
3.	whal	hwale	whale
4.	cube	cbue	cueb

Write the spelling words that rhyme with poke.

5. ____________ ____________

Write the spelling words that end with the same sound as late.

6. ____________ ____________

Write the spelling words that are opposites.

7. ____________ ____________

CA **LC 1.8** Spell three- and four-letter short-vowel words and grade-level-appropriate sight words correctly.

Name ______________________________

As you read Rose Robot Cleans Up, fill in the Conclusion Chart.

Inference	Inference

Conclusion

Inference	Inference

Conclusion

How does the Conclusion Chart help you better understand Rose Robot Cleans Up?

Name ______________________

You can use what you read and what you already know to help you **draw conclusions.**

Read each story. Draw a conclusion about the characters. Then fill in the circle of the sentence that makes the most sense with the story.

1. Jane bikes to school. She likes to run races. She has fun jumping rope. Jane plays ball with her pals, too.

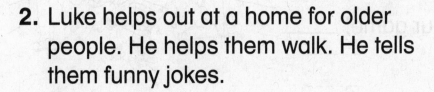

○ Jane is in good shape.

○ Jane likes to take care of dogs.

2. Luke helps out at a home for older people. He helps them walk. He tells them funny jokes.

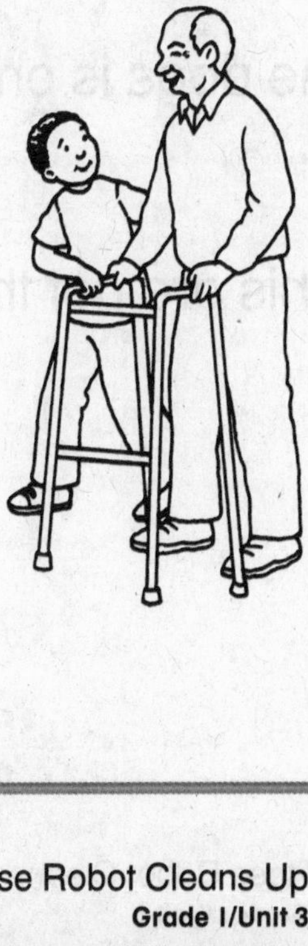

○ Luke is like the older people.

○ Luke likes to help older people.

Name ______________________________

Find the mistakes. Cross out the verb if it is wrong. Write the correct verb above it. Circle any letters that should be capital. Add the correct end mark if one is missing. (Hint: Each sentence has two mistakes.)

1. The little kids is in the den _____

2. don't let the dogs in here _____

3. hide the game, quick _____

4. it are too late. _____

5. the dogs is on our game! _____

6. This are not that funny _____

Name ____________________

As I read, I will pay attention to the exclamation marks.

What animal is small like a rat and lives
09 in a hole like a hare?
15 A mole! A mole is a small animal that
24 digs a hole with its teeth. It uses its nose
34 to find its lunch! A mole likes to sniff out
44 bugs and grubs to eat. In its hole, a mole
54 makes a nest with grass and sticks. You can
63 find moles in flat lands with grass! 70

Comprehension Check

1. Where does a mole live?
2. What does a mole eat?

	Words Read	–	Number of Errors	=	Words Correct Score
First Read		–		=	
Second Read		–		=	

CA **R 1.16** Read aloud with fluency in a manner that sounds like natural speech.

Name ______________________________

A **floor plan** is a drawing that shows where things are in a room.

Use the floor plan to complete each sentence.

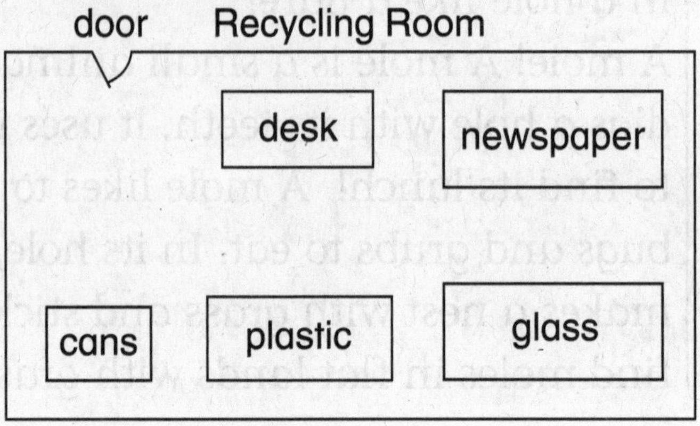

1. The cans bin is next to the ______________ bin.

2. If you can't tell which bin something goes in,

   ____

   ask for help at the ______________.

3. Put  in the ______________ bin.

4. These  go in the ______________ bin.

5. The smallest bin is for ______________.

Name ______________________________

Three letters can form a **blend**.
Listen for all three consonant sounds in each blend.

spring 

scratch 

splash 

Write the new word on the line.
Connect the word to the matching picture.

1. scr + atch = ______________________

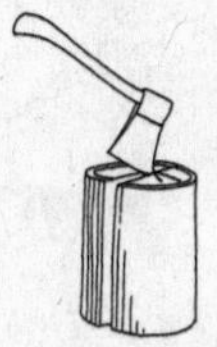

2. str + ipe = ______________________

3. spr + ing = ______________________

4. spl + it = ______________________

R 1.10 Generate the sounds from all the letters and letter patterns, including consonant blends and long- and short-vowel patterns (i.e., phonograms), and blend those sounds into recognizable words.

Name ______________________________

strike	string	splash	split	scrub
scrap	nose	cute	does	girl

Read each row of words.
Put an X on the word that does not belong.

1.	splash	split	spill
2.	take	cute	mute
3.	string	ship	strike
4.	hose	sled	nose
5.	school	scrub	scrap
6.	girl	grand	whirl

CA **LC 1.8** Spell three- and four-letter short-vowel words and grade-level-appropriate sight words correctly.

Name ____________________

Match each sentence to the picture that it explains.

1. The **girl** can do lots of tricks. **a.**

2. The dog jumps into the **water**. **b.**

3. Will my **friend** drop the books? **c.**

4. **Does** the **boy** have fun with that rope? **d.**

5. The kids have fun **by** the lake. **e.**

6. Can you have **any** fun with a pet? **f.**

CA **R 1.11** Read common, irregular sight words (e.g., *the, have, said, come, give, of*).

Name ______________________________

A contraction is a short way of saying and writing two words.

Two words: **are not** **does not**

Contractions: **aren't** **doesn't**

Draw a box around the contractions you find.

1. We can't go skating now.

2. Gram wasn't on the bus.

3. I didn't see her.

4. Why hasn't Gram called?

5. Isn't that Gram?

6. I couldn't find my skates.

CA **LC 1.3** Identify and correctly use contractions (e.g., *isn't, aren't, can't, won't*) and singular possessive pronouns (e.g., *my/mine, his/her, hers, your/s*) in writing and speaking.

Name ______________________________

When you add **-ed** or **-ing** to a word that ends with a vowel and a consonant, double the final consonant.

run + ing = ru**nn**ing — My dog is **running** fast.

chop + ed = cho**pp**ed — Sam **chopped** the log.

Read the sentence. Write the correct form of the word in the sentence.

1. Mike is ________________ the ball with a bat.
hit

2. The girl ________________ the nice red mug.
chip

3. The kids are ________________ the parts
put
of the kite together.

4. My dog just ________________ over his dish.
tip

CA **R 1.10** Generate the sounds from all the letters and letter patterns, including consonant blends and long- and short-vowel patterns (i.e., phonograms), and blend those sounds into recognizable words.

Name ______________________________

Practice

Spelling: 3-Letter Blends

A. Circle the spelling word that is spelled correctly.

1. scrub brusc

2. pascr scrap

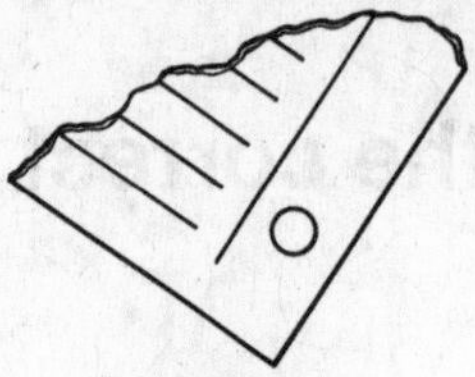

3. trings string

4. splash plashs

B. Pick a letter from the box to correctly write a spelling word.

k	**e**	**l**	**r**

5. gi ______ l

6. stri ______ e

7. do ______ s

8. sp ______ it

CA **LC 1.8** Spell three- and four-letter short-vowel words and grade-level-appropriate sight words correctly.

Name ____

As you read Kids Have Fun!, fill in the Compare and Contrast Chart.

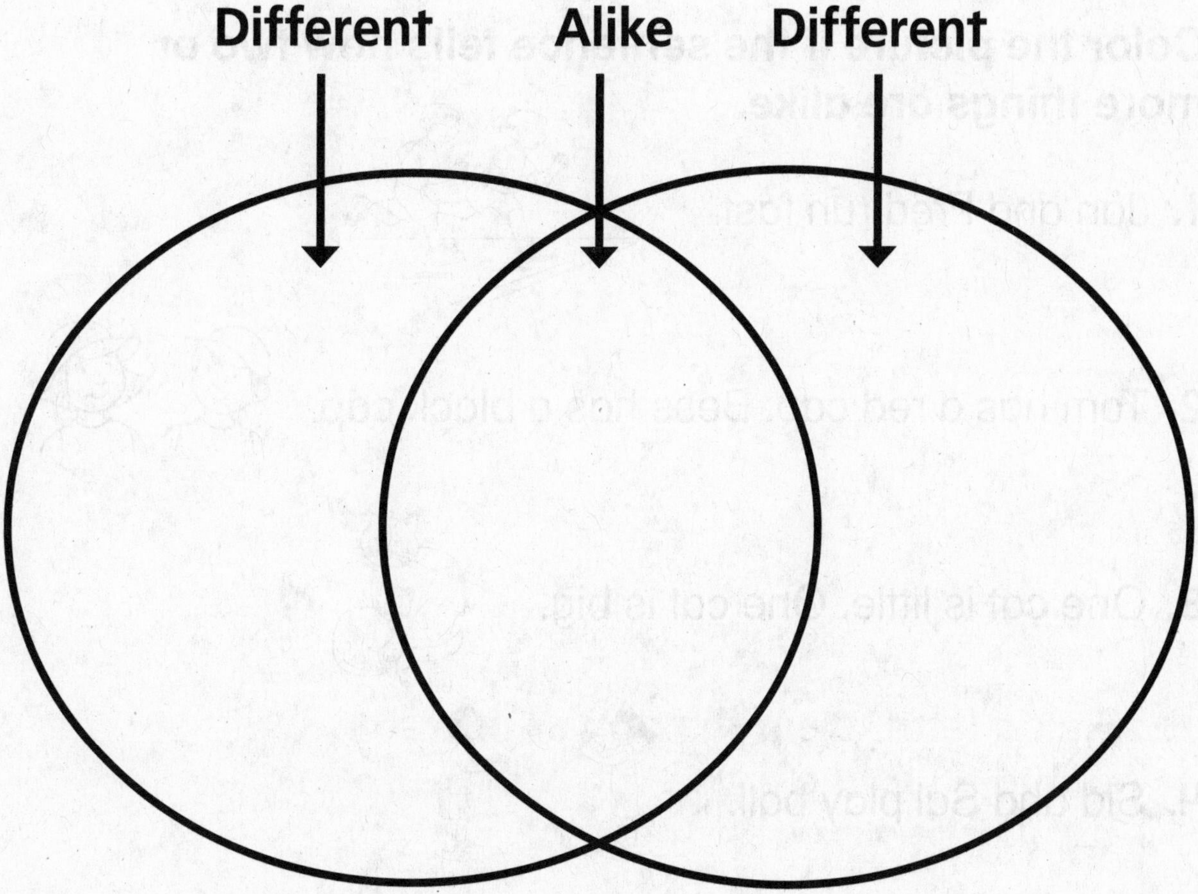

How does the Compare and Contrast Chart help you better understand Kids Have Fun!?

Name ________________________________

When you **compare** two or more things, you tell how they are **alike**.

When you **contrast** two or more things, you tell how they are **different**.

Color the picture if the sentence tells how two or more things are alike.

1. Jan and Fred run fast.

2. Tom has a red cap. Bess has a black cap.

3. One cat is little. One cat is big.

4. Sid and Sal play ball.

5. All the kids go to school.

6. Both girls like to play.

CA R 2.0 Reading Comprehension

Name ______________________________

A **contraction** is a short way of writing and saying two words.
Use an **apostrophe** (') to take the place of letters that are left out of a contraction.

Circle the contractions that are not correct.
Write the contractions correctly.
Write C if the contraction is correct.

1. Mom doesnt' like us to be late. ______________

2. You arent going to miss the bus! ______________

3. The bus isnt here yet. ______________

4. It wasn't on time. ______________

5. We are glad it did'nt splash us. ______________

CA **LC 1.3** Identify and correctly use contractions (e.g., *isn't, aren't, can't, won't*) and singular possessive pronouns (e.g., *my/mine, his/her, hers, your/s*) in writing and speaking.

Name ______________________________

Practice

Fluency: Choral Read: Intonation

As I read, I will pay attention to punctuation.

People all over like holidays. People come
07 together to do things on holidays. People
14 have holiday fun! What do people do on holidays?
23 Today people give thanks for the things they
31 have. They have lots of good things to eat.
40 Today boys and girls get together at a
48 show. It is fun when they sing holiday songs at the show.
60 What things do you do on holidays? 67

Comprehension Check

1. Why do people like holidays?

2. What do the boys and girls do at the holiday show?

	Words Read	–	Number of Errors	=	Words Correct Score
First Read		–		=	
Second Read		–		=	

CA **R 1.16** Read aloud with fluency in a manner that sounds like natural speech.

Name ____

Writers use interesting and colorful words.
The **fluffy white** clouds float in the sky.

Circle the two words that a writer could use to describe each picture.

1. fast soft red

2. many little wet

3. black one hot

4. three big hot

5. little many big

6. hot stink yummy

Name ______________________________

The letters **ay** and **ai** stand for the **long /a/** sound.

Use a word from the box to complete each sentence.

snail	pay	paint	clay

1. Ray will use some ________________.

2. He will ________________ the vase gray.

3. She will ________________ for the tray.

4. A ________________ is on the pail.

CA **R 1.10** Generate the sounds from all the letters and letter patterns, including consonant blends and long- and short-vowel patterns (i.e., phonograms), and blend those sounds into recognizable words.

Name ______________________________

mail	rain	chain	way	play
day	split	string	walked	eight

Use the clues to write a spelling word on the line.

1. starts like **splash** + sounds like **hit** ____________

2. starts like **want** + sounds like **say** ____________

3. starts like **dog** + sounds like **say** ____________

4. starts like **chin** + sounds like **main** ____________

5. starts like **make** + sounds like **pail** ____________

CA LC 1.8 Spell three- and four-letter short-vowel words and grade-level-appropriate sight words correctly.

Name ______________________________

Write a word from the box to complete each sentence.

once	upon	carry	eight	across	saw	walked

1. ____________ there were two chipmunks.

2. They ____________ some nuts to eat.

3. The nuts were ____________ the river.

4. The chipmunks wanted to ____________ the nuts back.

5. They ____________ on a log.

6. They put the nuts ____________ their heads.

7. They made ____________ trips.

CA R 1.11 Read common, irregular sight words (e.g., *the, have, said, come, give, of*).

Name ______________________________

As you read Drakes Tail, fill in the Predictions Chart.

What I Predict	What Happens

How does the Predictions Chart help you understand what happens in Drakes Tail?

Name ________________________________

A **prediction** is a guess about what will happen next.
There is pizza on a plate. A good **prediction** would be that someone will eat the pizza.

Draw a line connecting each sentence with the one that tells what will happen next.

1. The block falls down.	Tim will pick it up.
2. The frog sees a pond.	The vet will help.
3. A dog is sick.	It will hop in.
4. Dad gets a cake.	She will run fast.
5. Jan gets a doll.	She will play with it.
6. Peg is late for school.	He will eat it.

Make your own prediction.

7. Jake has a gift from his friend Meg.

____

Name ______________________________

The verbs **was** and **were** tell about the past.

Was tells about one person, place, or thing.

Were tells about more than one person, place, or thing.

Examples: Little Red **was** in the nest.
Mom and Dad **were** there, too.

Circle the verb that belongs in the sentence.

1. The sun (was, were) up.
2. Three eggs (was, were) in the nest.
3. One egg (was, were) not in the nest.
4. Dad (was, were) away from the nest.
5. Mom and Little Red (was, were) on a branch.

Name ______________________________

Circle the word that completes each sentence. Then write the word.

1. A dog can run ____________ than a cat.

faster fastest

2. A cat can run ____________ than a duck.

faster fastest

3. The dog is the ____________ of them all.

faster fastest

4. That little bed is ____________ than my bed.

softer softest

5. The big bed is the ____________ of them all.

softer softest

CA **R 1.10** Generate the sounds from all the letters and letter patterns, including consonant blends and long- and short-vowel patterns (i.e., phonograms), and blend those sounds into recognizable words.

Name ______________________________

A. Which word has the long a sound spelled correctly? Write the word on the line.

1. wai way ______________

2. rain rayn ______________

3. day dai ______________

4. mayl mail ______________

5. play plai ______________

6. chayn chain ______________

B. Circle the word that is spelled correctly.

7. eagth eiht eight

8. wakled walked wolked

CA **LC 1.8** Spell three- and four-letter short-vowel words and grade-level-appropriate sight words correctly.

Name ___________________________

A **dictionary** is a book that gives the meaning of words. Some words have more than one meaning.

Read the definitions below.

bark 1. the outside cover of a tree: The **bark** on the tree fell off. **2.** to make the sound that a dog makes: His dog will **bark** at all cats.

seal 1. an animal that lives in the ocean most of the time and swims very well: The **seal** swam over the wave. **2.** to close something so that it can not be opened: I had to **seal** the box with tape to close it.

Choose the correct definition for the word. Fill in the circle.

1. bark ○ drop a pole ○ be like a dog

2. bark ○ on a tree ○ in a pot

3. seal ○ run away ○ close a box very well

4. seal ○ a blue ship ○ an animal that swims

Use a word from above in a sentence.

____

Name ______________________________

As I read, I will pay attention to questions in the passage.

Hank and Fay have to work to make a trail
10 on the land.
13 Hank asks, "What do we do?"
19 "I will show you," says Fay. "We must cut down
29 all of the plants and shrubs in our way."
38 "Why do we have to do that?" asks Hank.
47 "Do you want to get a scrape or scratch from
57 a branch when you walk on this trail?" asks Fay.
67 "No way!" yells Hank.
71 Fay says, "Then we have to cut the plants on
81 our path."
83 "I see," says Hank. "Let's go!" 89

Comprehension Check

1. Why will Hank and Fay cut down the plants?

2. What will happen if they don't cut the plants down?

	Words Read	–	Number of Errors	=	Words Correct Score
First Read		–		=	
Second Read		–		=	

CA **R 1.16** Read aloud with fluency in a manner that sounds like natural speech.

Name ____________________

Use **was** to tell about one.

Use **were** to tell about more than one.

Capitalize proper nouns.

Find four mistakes in the story. Circle the mistakes. Write the sentences correctly on the lines.

Hal lives on plum lane. Jon came to play. The two boys was out back. They saw a robin in a nest. Lots of bugs were in the grass. One bug were not nice. It wanted to bite hal on the nose.

1. ____________________

2. ____________________

3. ____________________

4. ____________________

CA LC 1.0 Written and Oral English Language Conventions

Name ______________________________

Captions tell readers more about a photograph or picture.

Circle the caption that tells about the picture.

1. a snake
a baby deer

2. Big Bass Lake
the waterslide

3. my new bike
Big Buck Forest

4. the swimming pool
the campfire

5. our campsite
last day of school

6. Dad's big catch!
Sam's new dog

Name ________________________

Practice

Phonics:
Long *e*: *-e*, *ee*, *ea*

Listen to the sound the letters **ee**, **ea**, and -**e** stand for.

teeth 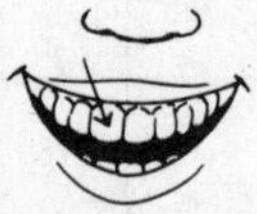 seal  he 

Circle the word that names each picture. Then write the word.

1. sheet she ________________

2. peel peek ________________

3. bean beak ________________

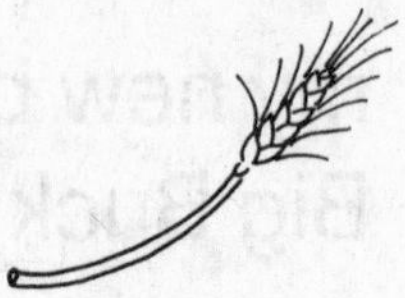

4. weak wheat ________________

5. seat seed ________________

6. eat eel ________________

CA **R 1.10** Generate the sounds from all the letters and letter patterns, including consonant blends and long- and short-vowel patterns (i.e., phonograms), and blend those sounds into recognizable words.

Name ____________________

me	we	feed	keep	seat
beak	rain	play	give	write

Write the words that have the long e sound.

1. ____________ 2. ____________

3. ____________ 4. ____________

5. ____________ 6. ____________

Write the words that have the long a sound.

7. ____________ 8. ____________

Write the words that do not have the long a or long e sound.

9. ____________ 10. ____________

CA LC 1.8 Spell three- and four-letter short-vowel words and grade-level-appropriate sight words correctly.

Name ________________________________

pretty	says	about	give	write	were

Use the words from the box to complete the sentences.

1. Here is a book ________________ cats.

2. "What is it?" ________________ Gram.

3. "Did you ________________ it?" I ask.

4. I ________________ her the book.

5. The cover is ________________.

6. We ________________ glad we could read it.

CA R 1.11 Read common, irregular sight words (e.g., *the, have, said, come, give, of*).

Name ______________________________

As you read Gram and Me, fill in the Character and Setting Chart.

What the Characters Do	Where They Do It
1.	1.
2.	2.
3.	3.
4.	4.

How does the Character and Setting Chart help you retell Gram and Me?

CA **R 3.1** Identify and describe the elements of plot, setting, and character(s) in a story, as well as the story's beginning, middle, and ending.

Name ______________________________

The **setting** is where a story takes place.

The **characters** are the people or animals in a story.

Think about what a school setting is like. Circle the people and things you would find in a school.

desk 

girl 

pen 

animal 

bike 

book 

skate 

boy 

CA **R 3.1** Identify and describe the elements of plot, setting, and character(s) in a story, as well as the story's beginning, middle, and ending.

Name ______________________________

The verbs **has** and **have** tell about the present.

Has tells about one person, place, or thing.

Have tells about more than one person, place, or thing.

Examples: Lulu **has** an old glass.

Pru and Zack **have** some cans.

Underline the verb if it tells about one.
Circle the verb if it tells about more than one.

1. The kids have work to do.

2. Pru has a black bag for the cans.
3. Zack has lots of cans.
4. Lulu and Dad have glass things.
5. Mom has a box for glass.
6. The two girls have big piles of stuff.

Name ____________________

Circle the word that names each picture.
Then write the word.

1. 

bean beet

____

2. 

deer deal

____

3. 

he heat

____

4. 

bee beat

____

5. 

steep steam

____

6. 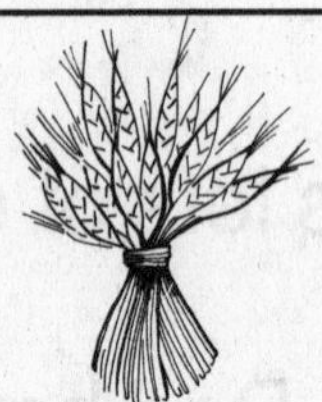

where wheat

____

7. 

seem seal

____

8. 

peel peach

____

CA **R 1.10** Generate the sounds from all the letters and letter patterns, including consonant blends and long- and short-vowel patterns (i.e., phonograms), and blend those sounds into recognizable words.

Name ______________________________

me	we	feed	keep	seat
beak	main	day	friends	knew

Put an <u>X</u> on the word that is spelled wrong in each row. Then write the word correctly.

1.	flip	fead	far	________
2.	seet	sent	sound	________
3.	glad	get	giv	________
4.	mail	make	mee	________
5.	knewe	kick	walk	________
6.	black	beek	bike	________
7.	wea	went	way	________
8.	woke	know	keap	________

CA **LC 1.8** Spell three- and four-letter short-vowel words and grade-level-appropriate sight words correctly.

Name ______________________________

Practice

Vocabulary Strategy: Context Clues

Context clues are words in a sentence that help you figure out the meaning of a new word.

Use context clues to figure out the meaning of the underlined word. Fill in the circle next to the correct answer.

1. Plants need water and sunlight to grow and stay alive.

○ living

○ outside

2. Mom picked a bunch of roses from the garden.

○ something that is red

○ a group of things

3. That baseball player is famous. Everyone knows who he is.

○ very well known

○ sad

4. I like puzzles so I like to read mystery books.

○ stories, plays, or movies that have a puzzle to solve

○ stories that are very funny

CA R 2.4 Use context to resolve ambiguities about word and sentence meanings.

Name ______________________________

As I read, I will pay attention to the dialogue.

"That box is for me," Nick shouted. "I
08 can take it now." Gus went on his way.
17 Beth looked at the big, big box. "You will never
27 lift that box," Beth said.
32 "So I will try to push it," Nick said. "Perhaps I
43 should try to pull it, too?"
49 But the box never moved. Nick was too little
58 and the box was so big.
64 "I can not do this myself. I need you, Beth," said
75 Nick. "This needs a push and a pull."
83 Nick and Beth worked together. Just then flakes
91 of snow fell. Nick and Beth woke up. 99

Comprehension Check

1. Why can't Nick move the box?

2. How do Nick and Beth move the box?

	Words Read	–	Number of Errors	=	Words Correct Score
First Read		–		=	
Second Read		–		=	

CA R 1.16 Read aloud with fluency in a manner that sounds like natural speech.

Name ______________________________

Find the mistakes.

A Change the verb to **has** or **have.**

B Begin with a capital letter.

C Add an end mark.

D Do not change.

(1) Some people do not care about our land (2) do you see all the junk on the sand? (3) Now, Carlos and Rosa has to pick it up. (4) doesn't the sand look good now (5) Carlos and Rosa have cans and glass to take home. (6) Mom have a good use for them.

Write the letter or letters that tell how you would fix the mistake.

1. ____________ 2. ____________

3. ____________ 4. ____________

5. ____________ 6. ____________

CA LC 1.0 Written and Oral English Language Conventions

Name ______________________________

A **numerical list** is a series of things written in **1, 2, 3** order.

Make two lists. Use the words below to help you.

pen	pants	tape
hat	desk	socks

Things for a Trip

1. ______________________
2. ______________________
3. ______________________

Things for School

1. ______________________
2. ______________________
3. ______________________

Draw a picture of something else you need at school.

Name ______________________

The long **o** vowel sound is spelled **o**, **oa**, and **ow**.

cold **coat** **snow**

coat mow hold snow fold toad

Write a word from the box to name each picture.

1.

2.

3.

4.

5.

6.
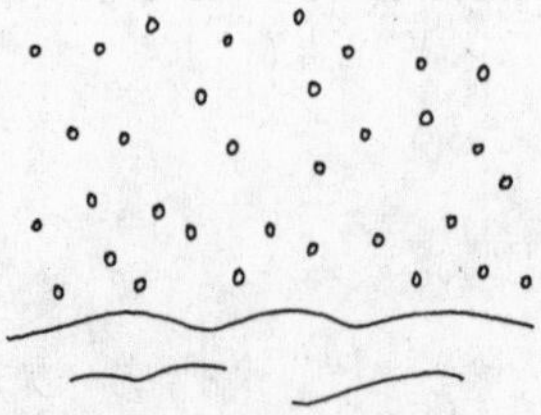

R 1.10 Generate the sounds from all letters and letter patterns, including consonant blends and long- and short-vowel patterns (i.e., phonograms), and blend those sounds into recognizable words.

Name ______________________________

low	row	boat	coat	no
go	we	keep	move	better

Write the spelling words that rhyme with show.

1. ______________ 2. ______________

3. ______________ 4. ______________

Write the spelling words that rhyme with goat.

5. ______________ 6. ______________

Write the spelling words that do not have the long o sound.

7. ______________ 8. ______________

9. ______________ 10. ______________

CA **LC 1.8** Spell three- and four-letter short-vowel words and grade-level-appropriate sight words correctly.

Name ______________________

better	buy	change	difficult	move	ripe

Use a word from the box to complete each sentence.

Did you just ______________ here? We have

a ______________ problem. We want to

______________ an ugly lot into a pretty lot. I have

an idea. We can use our money to ______________

seeds. We can plant peppers and pick them when they are

______________. Flowers can make the garden even

______________!

CA R 1.11 Read common, irregular sight words (e.g., *the, have, said, come, give, of*).

Name ______________________________

As you read <u>César Chávez</u>, fill in the Retelling Chart.

Retell
____
____
____
____

How does the Retelling Chart help you understand <u>César</u> <u>Chávez</u>?

CA **R 2.1** Identify text that uses sequence or other logical order.

Name ______________________________

Practice

Comprehension: Retell Information

When you **retell** a selection, tell the events in order. Use your own words.

Look at the pictures. Write what happens in each picture.

1. 

First, ______________________________

Next, ______________________________

Last, ______________________________

2. 

First, ______________________________

Next, ______________________________

Last, ______________________________

CA R 2.1 Identify text that uses sequence or other logical order.

Name ______________________

The verbs **go** and **do** have different forms to tell about the present and the past.

Present	Past
He **goes**. We **go**.	We all **went**.
She **does**. They **do**.	We all **did**.

Write the verb that tells about the present.

1. Jay ______________ outside to play. (goes, went)

2. Al ______________ not like to splash. (does, did)

3. We ______________ have fun in the rain. (do, did)

Write the verb that tells about the past.

4. When ______________ the sun come out? (does, did)

5. May and Lulu ______________ for a walk. (go, went)

6. I ______________ in when it got cold. (go, went)

CA LC 1.0 Written and Oral English Language Conventions

Name ______________________________

Some words have two parts, or **syllables**. You can break a word into syllables to help you read it.

A. Put the two syllables together. Write the word on the line. Then match the word to the picture it names.

1. car rot ______________________

2. pi lot ______________________

3. bas ket ______________________

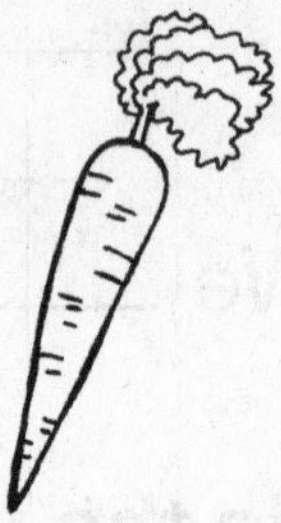

4. kick ing ______________________

B. Divide each word into syllables. Then write each syllable.

rabbit

__________ • __________

began

__________ • __________

Name ______________________________

Find the 8 spelling words in the puzzle.

A. Draw a circle around each word.

d	g	o	v	q	p	c	j	z
k	i	m	d	x	y	l	s	r
f	v	p	e	r	f	b	k	o
j	s	b	l	u	n	o	v	w
x	l	o	w	i	k	e	b	g
u	i	a	z	q	u	f	e	d
f	q	t	j	c	o	a	t	x
n	c	s	v	i	s	l	t	i
y	x	d	g	b	z	q	e	s
p	j	f	m	o	v	e	r	k

B. Write the spelling words from the puzzle.

1. ______________ 2. ______________

3. ______________ 4. ______________

5. ______________ 6. ______________

7. ______________ 8. ______________

CA **LC 1.8** Spell three- and four-letter short-vowel words and grade-level-appropriate sight words correctly.

Name ______________________________

Context clues are words that help you figure out the meaning of a new word. Context clues may be found in the same sentence or in nearby sentences.

Use the underlined context clues to figure out the meaning of the word in bold letters. Then match the word to its meaning. Write the correct letter on the line.

a. give what someone wants or can use
b. dirt
c. gather plants that are ready
d. plants used for food
e. plan for a group to do

1. Our town planned a **project** we could work on together. ____
2. The **crops** from our gardens will feed people who are hungry. ____
3. These bushes **provide** the berries we need to make pies. ____
4. When they are full and ripe, we will **harvest** them. ____
5. The **soil** in this field is very good for growing plants. ____

CA R 2.4 Use context to resolve ambiguities about word and sentence meanings.

Name ______________________________

As I read, I will pay attention to the phrasing.

It is Sunday. People on TV forecast the
08 weather. They let you know Sunday will be a
17 hot, sunny day.
20 Now you know what the weather will be. It's
29 a great day for swimming in the cold water!
38 Now, it is Monday. It is hot, but not sunny.
48 There are gray clouds everywhere. It may
55 rain.
56 It is Tuesday now. It is a rainy, wet day.
66 People will have to use their raincoats. 73

Comprehension Check

1. What can you do on a hot, sunny day?

2. What would you use on a rainy day?

	Words Read	–	Number of Errors	=	Words Correct Score
First Read		–		=	
Second Read		–		=	

CA **R 1.16** Read aloud with fluency in a manner that sounds like natural speech.

Name ______________________________

The verbs **go** and **do** use different forms to tell about the present and the past. The names of people and places begin with capital letters.

Read the story. Circle four sentences with mistakes. Write the sentences correctly.

One day, West Wind goed wild. "I will make it very cold," west wind said. That will be fun." That do not sound like fun to Sunray. So sunray shined and shined. Soon it got very warm. "Now that's fun!" she said.

1. ______________________________

2. ______________________________

3. ______________________________

4. ______________________________

CA LC 1.0 Written and Oral English Language Conventions

Name ____________________

A **telephone directory** lists names, addresses, and telephone numbers.

Vann,	Jay	17 Elm Ave.	555-5436
Vann,	Max	17 Elm Ave.	555-5436
Wade,	Jake	245 Main St.	555-7401
Wade,	Lon	29 Sunset Ave.	555-4269
Wade,	May	9 Sunrise St.	555-9711

Use the directory to complete each question.

1. How many people have the last name Wade? ______

2. What is May Wade's phone number? ______________

3. Where does Jake Wade live? ______________

4. Who has the same address and telephone number?

____

____

Practice

Phonics: Long *i*

Name ______________________________

Say the words. Then listen to the **long /i/** sound.

child fly high

Write the word that completes the sentence.

1. Meg's kite will ____________ over the trees.

try fly cry

2. Mike will ____________ up his new truck.

win wind white

3. We eat lunch together on a ____________ hill.

might high fly

4. Let's wave to that plane in the ____________.

my sky cry

5. The ____________ can walk to his house.

mild child cut

CA **R 1.10** Generate the sounds from all the letters and letter patterns, including consonant blends and long- and short-vowel patterns (i.e., phonograms), and blend those sounds into recognizable words.

Name ______________________

Practice

Spelling: Long *i*: *i*, *y*, *igh*

find	kind	night	right	by
my	no	boat	never	should

A. Circle the spelling words in each row.

1. wide	find	kind
2. by	line	my
3. stone	no	row
4. night	right	bite
5. boat	goat	vote
6. never	should	ever

B. Write two long i spelling words that have four letters.

7. ______________ **8.** ______________

C. Write two long i spelling words that have five letters.

9. ______________ **10.** ______________

CA **LC 1.8** Spell three- and four-letter short-vowel words and grade-level-appropriate sight words correctly.

Write the letter of the word from the box that completes each sentence.

a. head	**b.** never	**c.** should	**d.** ball
e. shout	**f.** meadow	**g.** Perhaps	

1. The boys and girls ______ for the team.

2. The big kite was flying high over Kim's ______.

3. Ben is ______ late for the school bus.

4. We ______ get a new bat and ______ at the shop.

5. ______ we can ride together in the green ______ today.

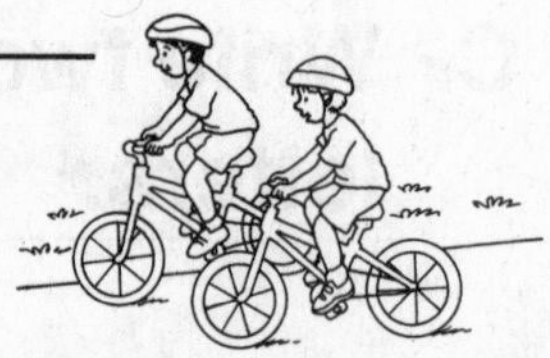

Name ________________________________

As you read <u>The Kite</u>, fill in the Problem and Solution Chart.

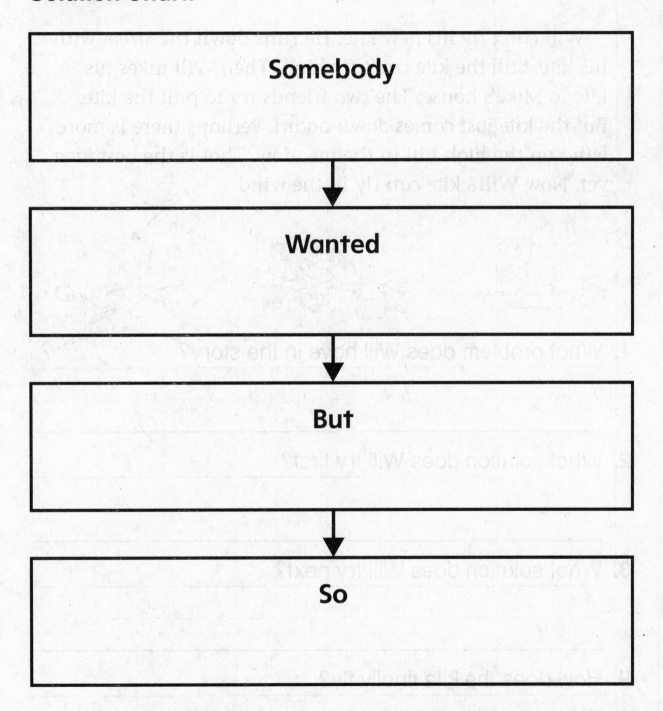

Somebody
↓
Wanted
↓
But
↓
So

How does the Problem and Solution Chart help you better understand <u>The Kite</u>?

CA **R 3.1** Identify and describe the elements of plot, setting, and character(s) in a story, as well as the story's beginning, middle, and ending.

Name ______________________

Read the story about Will's problem and solution. Then answer the questions.

Will can't fly his new kite. He runs down the street with his kite. Still the kite can't fly high. Then Will takes his kite to Mike's house. The two friends try to pull the kite. But the kite just comes down again. Perhaps there is more wind on the high hill in the meadow. That is the best idea yet. Now Will's kite can fly in the wind.

1. What problem does Will have in the story?

2. What solution does Will try first?

3. What solution does Will try next?

4. How does the kite finally fly?

R 3.1 Identify and describe the elements of plot, setting, and character(s) in a story, as well as the story's beginning, middle, and ending.

Name ______________________

The verb **see** has a special form to tell about the past.

Present	Past
She **sees**. We **see**.	They **saw**.

Circle the verb that tells about the past.

1. Jean (see, sees, saw) the leaf.
2. We (see, sees, saw) a small bug.
3. Pat (see, sees, saw) many lines on the leaf.

Circle the verb that tells about the present.

4. Sue (see, sees, saw) spots on the leaf.
5. Pat and Sue (see, sees, saw) a bug.
6. We also (see, sees, saw) the bug.

Name ______________________________

For words that end with a consonant followed by **y**, change the **y** to **i** before adding **-es**.

bun**ny** bunn**ies**

Read the word under each sentence. Change the word by adding -es. Then complete each sentence.

1. The twin ____________ smiled at me.
baby

2. Their ____________ are full.
tummy

3. Jenny ____________ math every day.
study

4. Tommy and Timmy are ____________.
buddy

5. The ____________ at the pet store were so cute.
puppy

CA R 1.14 Read inflectional forms (e.g., *-s*, *-ed*, *-ing*) and root words (e.g., *look*, *looked*, *looking*).

Name ______________________________

A. Find the word that is spelled wrong. Write the word correctly on the line.

1. I can ride mey bike fast. ____________

2. I cannot fynd the ball. ____________

3. The wind whipped biye and made ____________ the blades spin. ____________

4. I would nevver jump out ____________ of a plane! ____________

5. Do it rite to get a strike. ____________

B. Fill in the circle next to the word that is spelled correctly.

6. ○ kined
○ kinnd
○ kind

7. ○ nite
○ night
○ nytte

8. ○ find
○ fyned
○ fighnd

CA **LC 1.8** Spell three- and four-letter short-vowel words and grade-level-appropriate sight words correctly.

Name ______________________

A verb is a word that shows action.
You can add **-ed** or **-ing** to most verbs.
A verb with an **-ed** ending means the action happened in the past.

play + **ing** = playing

play + **ed** = played

A. Write each verb with -ing and -ed.

1. flash ______________ ______________

2. pull ______________ ______________

3. fill ______________ ______________

B. Use an -ing word and -ed word in sentences.

4. ______________________________

____

Name ____________________________________

As I read, I will pay attention to the dialogue.

Pig went out to fly a kite. Dog went with him.
11 "See how high my kite can fly!" Pig said. Then
21 Pig's kite got stuck high up in a tree. Dog went
32 up to get it.
36 "Don't fall, Dog!" yelled Pig. Toad came over to
45 look, too. "Pig's kite is so high up," he said.
55 "Dog might not get it." So Toad got a stick.
65 Toad gave the stick to Dog.
71 Then, Dog got Pig's kite.
76 "Thank you so much!" said Pig. "I am glad I
86 have such kind friends." 90

Comprehension Check

1. What is Pig's problem?

2. Who helped Pig solve the problem?

	Words Read	–	Number of Errors	=	Words Correct Score
First Read		–		=	
Second Read		–		=	

CA **R 1.16** Read aloud with fluency in a manner that sounds like natural speech.

Name ______________________________

Read the letter.

Two commas are missing. Three verbs are wrong.

Add the missing commas. Cross out the verbs that are wrong.

Write the verbs in the past tense on the lines below.

September 3 1922

Dear Nana,

Dad put up a little house in our elm tree. "It's a bat house," he say.

Last Monday, my friends came over. We saw five bats go in the house. We sees the bats hanging upside down.

I says, "Bats are fun to watch."

Your grandson

Joe

____

____

____

Name ______________________________

A chart gives information in an organized way.

Read the chart.

Things Frog Ate	Things Toad Ate
plums I	peaches II
apples II	plums III
grapes 𝍸 III	eggs III
eggs II	grapes 𝍸 𝍸

Count the things Frog and Toad ate and complete the sentences.

1. Frog ate ____________ eggs.

2. Toad ate ____________ grapes.

3. Frog ate ____________ plum.

4. Toad ate ____________ peaches.

Name ______________________________

Sometimes the letter **y** stands for the **long /e/** sound. happ**y**

Circle the word that answers the question. Then write the word.

1. What can you ride in? ____________

   buggy jelly

2. What can you spend? ____________

   muddy penny

3. What do you call a very small boy? ____________

   pony baby

4. What do you call a baby dog? ____________

   daisy puppy

5. What can you call a rabbit? ____________

   bunny easy

CA R 1.4 Distinguish initial, medial, and final sounds in single-syllable words.

Name ________________________

bumpy	penny	puppy	sandy	funny
bunny	my	night	or	because

Circle the words that end with the long e sound.

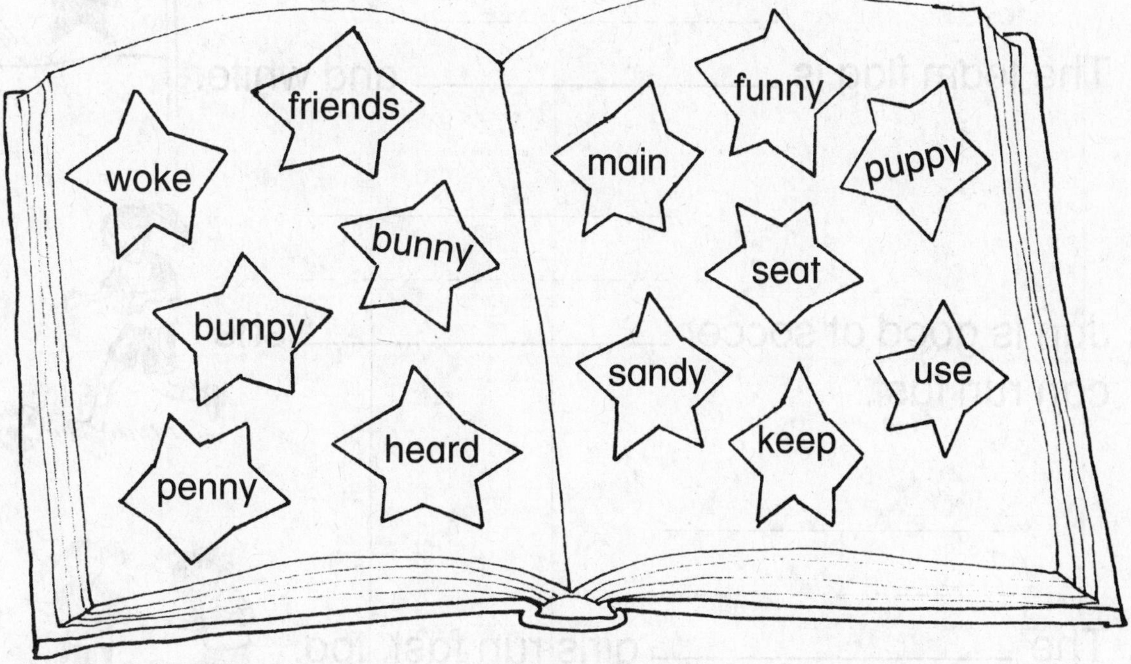

Write the words you circled.

1. ____________ 2. ____________ 3. ____________

4. ____________ 5. ____________ 6. ____________

CA **LC 1.8** Spell three- and four-letter short-vowel words and grade-level-appropriate sight words correctly.

Name ______________________________

blue	because	until	other	also	or

Write the word that completes each sentence.

1. The team flag is ______________ and white.

2. Jan is good at soccer ______________ she can run fast.

3. The ______________ girls run fast, too.

4. The team may ______________ may not win.

5. The girls think that having fun is ______________ a goal.

Name ______________________________

As you read Animal Teams, fill in the Retelling Chart.

Retell
______________________________ ______________________________ ______________________________ ______________________________

How does the information you wrote in this Retelling Chart help you retell Animal Teams?

Name ______________________________

When you **retell** a passage, you tell only the important parts.

Read the passage. Then look at it again. Underline the sentences that retell the passage.

What will we see in an ant nest?
The worker ants bring in things to eat.
Some take things to eat to the queen.
The queen does not get food.
She stays in the nest.
The queen ant lays eggs.

Draw three pictures to retell the story.

Name ______________________________

A **contraction** is a short way of saying and writing two words.

Many contractions are formed with **not**. An **apostrophe** (') takes the place of the letters that are left out.

Examples: do + not → don't

does + not → doesn't

Match the underlined words to contractions. Write the sentence letter on the line. The first one is done for you.

A. "This is not funny," said Bunny.

B. "You are not good friends."

C. "I did not do it," said Frog.

D. "I was not the one," said Skunk.

E. "We were not here," they said.

F. "We could not have opened the box."

1. isn't ___A___ **2.** wasn't ________

3. weren't ________ **4.** didn't ________

5. couldn't ________ **6.** aren't ________

CA **LC 1.3** Identify and correctly use contractions (e.g., *isn't, aren't, can't, won't*) and singular possessive pronouns (e.g., *my/mine, his/her, hers, your/s*) in writing and speaking.

Name ______________________________

If a verb ends in a **consonant + y**, change the **y** to **i** before adding **-ed**. **cry** + ed = cri**ed**

Write the word that completes each sentence.

1. The baby ____________.

   cried   cryed

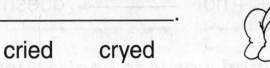

2. Han ____________ his hands.

   dryed   dried

3. Mom ____________ the top open.

   pried   pryed

4. Kelly ____________ the big bike.

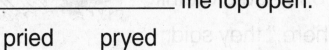

   tried   tryed

5. Dad ____________ the fish.

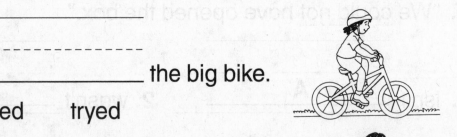

   fryed   fried

Name ______________________________

Look at each set of words.
One word in each set is spelled correctly.
Use a pencil to fill in the circle in front of that word.

1. ○ funney
○ funny
○ funy

2. ○ penny
○ pennie
○ peney

3. ○ pupuy
○ puppee
○ puppy

4. ○ ohr
○ or
○ orr

5. ○ because
○ becaus
○ becase

6. ○ bummpee
○ bumpeye
○ bumpy

7. ○ bunny
○ bunnie
○ bunea

8. ○ sandiye
○ sandy
○ sandeey

CA **LC 1.8** Spell three- and four-letter short-vowel words and grade-level-appropriate sight words correctly.

Name ______________________________

Context clues are words in a sentence that help you figure out the meaning of a new word.

Use the underlined context clues to figure out the meaning of the word in bold letters.

1. The apples are **falling** down to the ground.

2. The branches and leaves hide animals in the **forest**.

3. I **heard** the owl hoot.

4. The rabbit hopped into the bush **before** the fox saw it.

Now match the word to its meaning:

1. falling	**a.** listened with ears
2. forest	**b.** to go from a high place to a low place
3. heard	**c.** at an earlier time
4. before	**d.** a place where trees and plants grow

CA **R 2.4** Use context to resolve ambiguities about word and sentence meanings.

Name ______________________________

As I read, I will pay attention to questions in the passage.

All kinds of games can be fun.
07 A coach teaches a team to swim fast and dive.
17 Today they race back and forth again and again.
26 Does this game seem fun to you?
33 You can make riding a bike into a game. You can
44 ride laps on a track with a friend. Use a watch to see
57 who rides a lap faster!
62 Is this game for you?
67 Some games are team games. In baseball, you hit
76 a ball with a bat and run! Will you make a home run?
89 Can you think of a game that you like to play?
100 Then go play it! 104

Comprehension Check

1. Who teaches the swimmers their game?

2. Why do the bike riders use a watch?

	Words Read	–	Number of Errors	=	Words Correct Score
First Read		–		=	
Second Read		–		=	

CA **R 1.16** Read aloud with fluency in a manner that sounds like natural speech.

Name ___

A **contraction** is a short form of two words. Use an **apostrophe** (') to take the place of the **o** in contractions formed with **not**.

Make a check mark [✔] next to the sentence with the correct contraction. Circle the contraction.

1. The fox couldn't get the grapes.

   The fox couldnt get the grapes.

2. The boy wasn't telling a lie.

   The boy wasnt' telling a lie.

3. The rabbit did'nt win the race.

   The rabbit didn't win the race

4. The man doe'snt keep the talking fish.

   The man doesn't keep the talking fish.

5. The cat and mice aren't friends.

   The cat and mice arent friends.

CA **LC 1.3** Identify and correctly use contractions (e.g., *isn't, aren't, can't, won't*) and singular possessive pronouns (e.g., *my/mine, his/her, hers, your/s*) in writing and speaking.

Name ______________________

Poems often **repeat** words or sentences more than once.

Read the poem. Then answer the questions.

The Pelican and the Fish

The fish swims.
The pelican flies over.
The fish swims.
The pelican is hungry.
The fish swims.
The pelican dives down.
The fish swims.

____

The pelican ______________________
GULP!

1. Circle the sentences that repeat.

2. Complete the end of the poem.

Name ______________________

Practice

Phonics: *r*-controlled Vowels: *er*, *ir*, *ur*

The letters **er**, **ir**, and **ur** stand for the same sound.

cl**er**k b**ir**d t**ur**n

Circle the word that names the picture. Then write the word on the line.

1. 
girl
gull
____

2. 
cot
curl
____

3. 
fun
fern
____

4. 
spur
spot
____

5. 
hid
her
____

6. 
squirt
squint
____

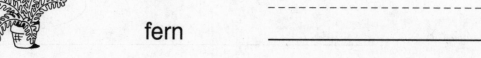

CA R 1.4 Distinguish initial, medial, and final sounds in single-syllable words.

Name ______________________________

her	fern	bird	dirt	fur
burn	funny	penny	full	through

A. Complete the spelling word by writing the letters that make the sound in heard and were.

1. b ______ n

2. f ______ r

3. d ______ t

4. h ______

5. f ______ n

6. b ______ d

B. Write the words that have double letters.

7. ______________

8. ______________

9. ______________

Name ______________________________

full poor another climbed through

A. Write the word that completes each sentence.

1. Little Skunk ____________ out of her den.

2. She was hungry and ____________.

3. She went over to ____________ den and looked in.

4. The den was ____________ of things to eat!

5. A small head poked ____________ the leaves.

B. Write a sentence to complete the story.

6. ______________________________

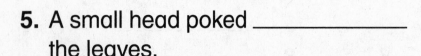

CA **R 1.11** Read common, irregular sight words (e.g., *the, have, said, come, give, of*).

Name ______________________________

As you read Kitten's First Full Moon, fill in the Cause and Effect Chart.

Cause		Effect
	→	
	→	
	→	
	→	
	→	

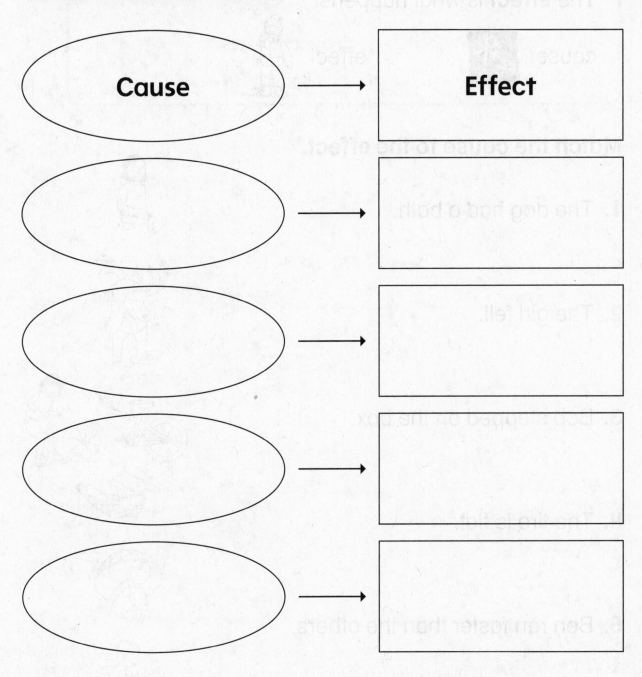

How does the information you wrote in this Cause and Effect Chart help you retell Kitten's First Full Moon?

Name ______________________________

The **cause** is why something happens.

The **effect** is what happens.

cause  effect 

Match the cause to the effect.

1. The dog had a bath.

2. The girl fell.

3. Bob stepped on the box.

4. The tire is flat.

5. Ben ran faster than the others.

6. It is raining.

Name ______________________________

An **adjective** is a word that tells about a noun.
A **noun** is a person, place, or thing.

That is a **great** painting.

adjective noun

Circle the adjective in each sentence. Underline the noun it tells about. The first one is done for you.

1. The boat is sailing on a blue sea.
2. A little girl stands on the deck.
3. The cool wind blows her hair.
4. The tall sails flap in the wind.
5. People wave from a sandy beach.
6. You are a good painter.

Name ______________________________

To add **-er** or **-est** to words that end in **e**, drop the **e** and then add **-er** or **-est**.

cut**e** + **er** = cut**er** That pup is **cuter** than this one.

cut**e** + **est** = cut**est** The cat is the **cutest** of all.

Add -er or -est to each word. Then write the new word in the sentence.

1. His pet is ______________ than the wild cat.
tame

2. The tree in the meadow is the ______________.
large

3. My dad is the ______________ of all.
brave

4. The ______________ bus should stop here.
late

5. Now my dog is ______________ than your dog.
clean

CA **R 1.14** Read inflectional forms (e.g., *-s*, *-ed*, *-ing*) and root words (e.g., *look*, *looked*, *looking*).

Name ______________________

A. Change one letter to spell the /ur/ sound correctly. Write the spelling word on the line.

1. fer ______________ 2. berd ______________

3. durt ______________ 4. hir ______________

5. furn ______________ 6. birn ______________

B. Circle the word that is spelled correctly. Write it on the line.

7. ful fulle full ______________

8. through throuhg thrugh ______________

CA **LC 1.8** Spell three- and four-letter short-vowel words and grade-level-appropriate sight words correctly.

Name ______________________________

Read the dictionary entries below.

middle halfway between two ends: We stood in the **middle** of the line.

mistake something thought or done incorrectly: I made one **mistake** on the spelling test.

protects to keep away from harm: The mother hen protects her eggs.

Use a word from the box to complete each sentence. You may use a word more than once.

1. Joan sat in the ______________ of her two friends.

2. The mother cat ______________ her babies.

3. Please draw a line down the ______________ of the paper.

4. If you make a ______________, try again.

Name ____________________

As I read, I will pay attention to patterns in the story.

Where do birds live? Birds live in many places.
09 A bird can live in a tree. It can use twigs and sticks to
23 make a nest on a branch. These birds will eat bugs they
35 find in the grass.
39 Some birds can live in the woods. Birds
47 that live in the woods might peck a hole in
57 a tree to make a home.
63 Other birds can even live on ice! They are called
73 penguins. They cannot fly, but they can dive
81 into the water to eat!
86 They swim in the water to look for krill. Krill are
97 small shrimp.
99 All birds lay eggs. 103

Comprehension Check

1. What are krill?

2. Where do birds find bugs to eat?

	Words Read	–	Number of Errors	=	Words Correct Score
First Read		–		=	
Second Read		–		=	

Name ______________________

A. Read the letter. Circle six words that should begin with capital letters.

Dear mike,

Would you like to come to the shoat Gallery with us? It is on front street in the city. dad says we will see some great paintings there. We are going in two weeks.

Your friend,

Sandy wan

B. Write the sentence correctly. Add an adjective to tell more about the underlined nouns.

1. The name of the girl who painted that daisy is joan reed.

CA LC 1.0 Written and Oral English Language Conventions

Name ______________________________

Captions tell you facts about a photo or picture.

Read the captions. Then answer the questions.

On May 28, Paul and Mom paint his bedroom.

1. Who is in the picture? ______________________

2. What are they doing? ______________________

3. What is the date? ______________________

On June 10, Pam and Joy make a sand castle at the beach.

4. Who are the children? ______________________

5. What are the children doing? ______________________

6. What is the date? ______________________

Name ___________________________

Practice

Phonics: *r*-controlled Vowel: *ar*

Together the letters **a** and **r** stand for the sound you hear in **car**. Listen for the **ar** sound in the word.

car 

Read the sentence. Then write the word that completes the sentence.

1. We can play in the ___________. yard / yarn

2. The ___________ is far away. smart / star

3. The ___________ has many teeth. start / shark

4. Wheat grows on a ___________. farm / barn

5. A ___________ is a fish. cart / carp

6. Nana gave me a blue ___________. scar / scarf

CA R 1.4 Distinguish initial, medial, and final sounds in single-syllable words.

Name ____________________

cart	art	barn	yarn	arm
harm	her	dirt	would	house

Circle the two words in each group that rhyme.

1. horn	harm	farm
2. dirt	mart	hurt
3. cart	part	clip
4. yarn	your	barn
5. hare	her	fur
6. house	pool	mouse

CA **LC 1.8** Spell three- and four-letter short-vowel words and grade-level-appropriate sight words correctly.

Name ______________________________

Read each sentence. Choose the word that completes the sentence. Circle the word.

1. Dan _____ like to play.

   would   house

2. The number of balls _____.

   grew   knew

3. Jean said she could _____ far.

   run   curious

4. "I _____ you were it!" she said.

   knew   kind

5. Mike likes to look. He is _____.

   friends   curious

6. Dean has another _____.

   idea   knew

7. "I'm so glad we went to Dean's _____," said Mike.

   friends   house

CA **R 1.11** Read common, irregular sight words (e.g., *the, have, said, come, give, of*).

Name ______________________________

As you read Meet Ben Franklin, fill in the Inference Chart.

Text Clues	What You Know	Inferences

How does the Inference Chart help you better understand Meet Ben Franklin?

Name ______________________________

Read the story. Then choose an answer to complete each sentence.

Jean puts a cast on a cat. Then she looks at a man's dog. The dog's teeth are bad. "Please brush your dog's teeth," she tells the man. Today she takes care of many pets. "Oh, no!" says Jean. "I did not eat lunch yet."

1. What does the author want you to know about Jean?
   - ○ Jean works in a lab.
   - ○ Jean is a vet.
   - ○ Jean likes to read.

2. Why does Jean put a cast on the cat?
   - ○ The cat goes to sleep.
   - ○ The cat wants to eat.
   - ○ The cat broke a leg.

3. Jean did not eat lunch because she _____.
   - ○ was not hungry
   - ○ forgot
   - ○ had no pets to take care of

4. What would be a good title for this story?
   - ○ The Cat with the Broken Leg
   - ○ A Busy Day for Jean
   - ○ The Fast Dog

Add **-er** to an adjective to compare two people, places, or things.

Example: Jon is **faster** than Mike.

Add **-est** to an adjective to compare three or more people, places, or things.

Example: Ed is the **fastest** boy on the team.

A. Write the adjectives that compare.

	add -er	**add -est**
1. low	____________	____________
2. sweet	____________	____________
3. kind	____________	____________

B. Underline the adjectives that compare.

4. My dog is slower than Tim's dog.
5. It is bigger than Pedro's dog.
6. It is the cutest dog in the bunch.

Name ______________________________

An **abbreviation** is a short form of writing a longer word.

Look at these abbreviations.

Mister → Mr. Missus → Mrs. Doctor → Dr.

A. Write the abbreviations for each word.

1. Doctor ____________

2. Missus ____________

3. Mister ____________

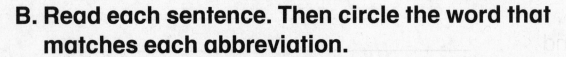

B. Read each sentence. Then circle the word that matches each abbreviation.

4. I will make a cake for <u>Mrs.</u> Smith.

Melissa Missus Miss

5. <u>Dr.</u> Shin helps me when I'm sick.

Doctor Missus Mister

6. We sent mail to <u>Mr.</u> Lee.

Doctor Saturday Mister

Name ______________________________

Read the story.
Circle the 8 words that are not spelled correctly.
Then write the words correctly on the lines.

The children made some beautiful art. Kim made herr art out of yarnn. "Can we hang it in the barrn?" she said.

"There is a lot of arte," Mark said. "I can't lift it. My armm is in a sling."

"I have an idea," Pam said. "Let's put it all in a carrt. Then we can pull it from the howse."

"This is a great plan," Mark said. "It does not haerm the art or my back."

1. ______________ 2. ______________

3. ______________ 4. ______________

5. ______________ 6. ______________

7. ______________ 8. ______________

CA **LC 1.8** Spell three- and four-letter short-vowel words and grade-level-appropriate sight words correctly.

Name ______________________________

A verb is a word that shows action. When a verb has the ending **-ed**, the action happened in the past. The **-ing** ending means the action is happening now. You can pick out the word parts of a verb to figure out its meaning.

Underline the word in each sentence that has a word ending. Circle the base word. Then write now if it is something that is happening now. Write past if it was something that happened in the past.

1. I am playing with my best friend. ____________

2. My cat climbed up the tree. ____________

3. Dad milked a cow. ____________

4. I am packing for my trip. ____________

5. We watched a good game. ____________

Name ______________________________

As I read, I will pay attention to the exclamation points.

"Look at all the butterflies!" I said to Amy.
09 "I hope I find a Painted Lady!"
16 "Is that one?" Amy asked.
21 "No," I said. "A Painted Lady is not red."
30 A butterfly landed on Amy.
35 "Look, Sara!" Amy said. "Is it a Painted Lady?"
44 "No," I said. "A Painted Lady doesn't have
52 black bands."
54 "I have never been here before," I said to a
64 helper. "Do you have a Painted Lady?"
71 "Yes," she said. "Keep looking! You will find one."
80 "There it is!" said Amy.
85 "No, it's not," I said. "A Painted Lady has
94 black and white spots." 98

Comprehension Check

1. What kind of butterfly are Amy and her friend hoping to find?

2. Does the Painted Lady have bands or spots?

	Words Read	–	Number of Errors	=	Words Correct Score
First Read		–		=	
Second Read		–		=	

CA **R 1.16** Read aloud with fluency in a manner that sounds like natural speech.

Name ______________________

Look for mistakes with adjectives that compare.
Look for mistakes with capital letters and end marks.

Write X if a sentence has any mistakes.

Write C if a sentence is correct.

1. what makes the sticks fly up ________

2. You have to roll and push. ________

3. Which of the three sticks will spin for the long time of all? ________

4. Ruby's stick makes a soft sound than mine does. ________

5. Catch the stick before it drops! ________

6. my stick has a wider top than yours ________

CA LC 1.0 Written and Oral English Language Conventions

Name ____________________

Bold print points out important words.

Read the story. Then write the answer to each question below.

Ben Franklin was an **inventor**. He came up with ideas for many things that would help to make people's lives better. His **Franklin Stove** was a much safer way for people to burn wood for heat and for cooking. Even now we use a **lightning rod** to protect houses and ships from lightning. He gave his inventions away for **free**.

1. What is an inventor?

____

2. What did people use as a safer way to burn wood?

____

3. What does a lightning rod do?

____

Name ______________________

The letters **or** stand for the middle sound in **horse**.

Circle the word that completes the sentence.
Then write the word on the line.

1. The ________________ is in the barn.

   porch horse fort

2. The ________________ is sharp.

   storm stork thorn

3. We play ________________ at the park.

   sports shorts sort

4. The lamp has a new ________________.

   cord fork corn

5. We can patch the ________________ pants.

   north torn for

Name ______________________________

born	corn	cork	fork	horn
pork	barn	arm	know	great

A. Circle the words that have the or sound.

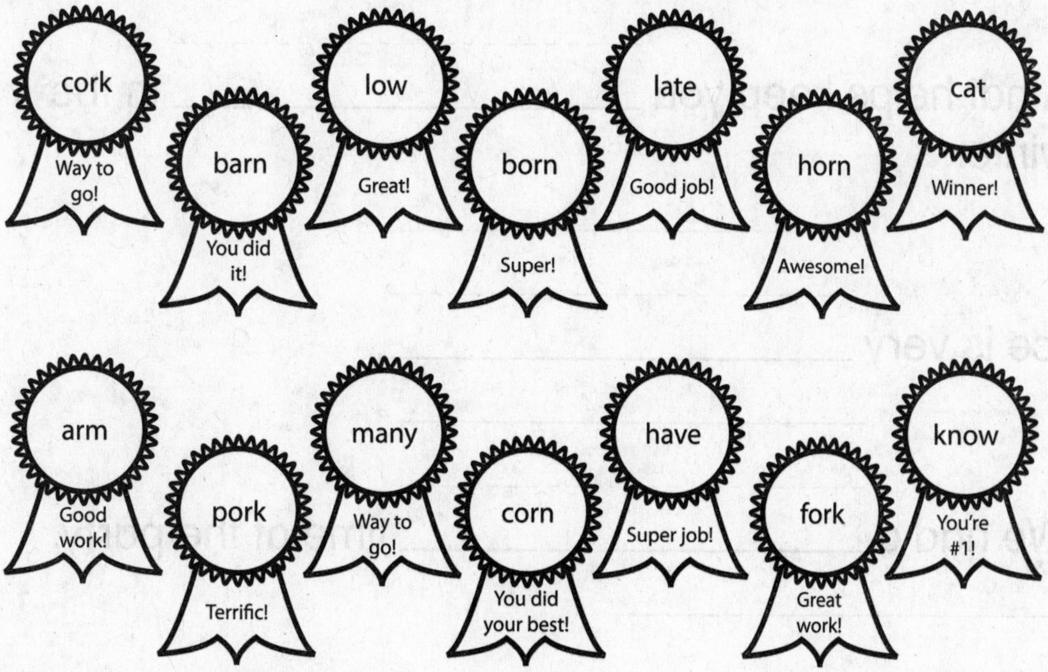

B. Write the words you circled.

1. ______________ 2. ______________ 3. ______________

4. ______________ 5. ______________ 6. ______________

CA **LC 1.8** Spell three- and four-letter short-vowel words and grade-level-appropriate sight words correctly.

Name ______________________________

A. Use words in the box to complete the sentences.

Their	cold	warm	great

1. A hat helps keep you ____________ in the winter.

2. Ice is very ____________.

3. We had a ____________ time at the party.

4. ____________ dog is black and white.

B. Match the word to its meaning.

5. sound — very great; dangerous
6. predict — something you hear
7. extreme — to guess what will happen next

CA R 1.11 Read common, irregular sight words (e.g., *the, have, said, come, give, of*).

As you read Stormy Weather, fill in the Compare and Contrast Chart.

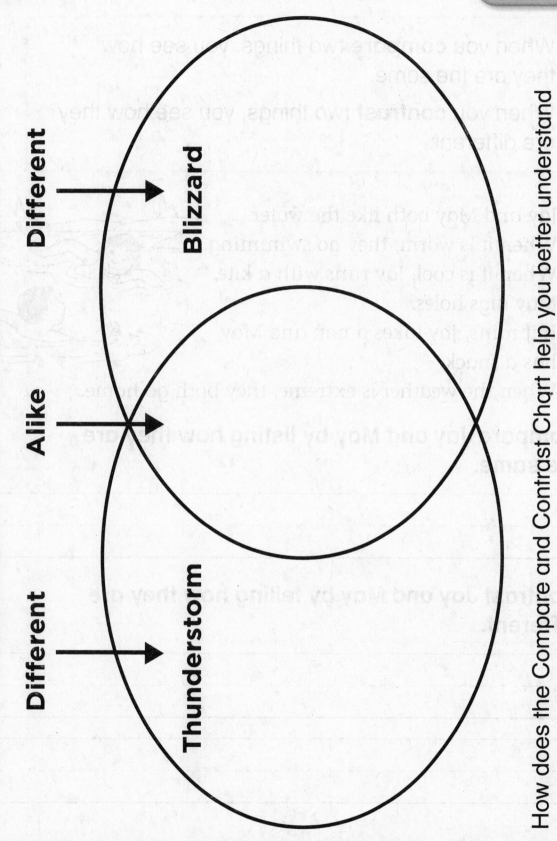

Different **Alike** **Different**

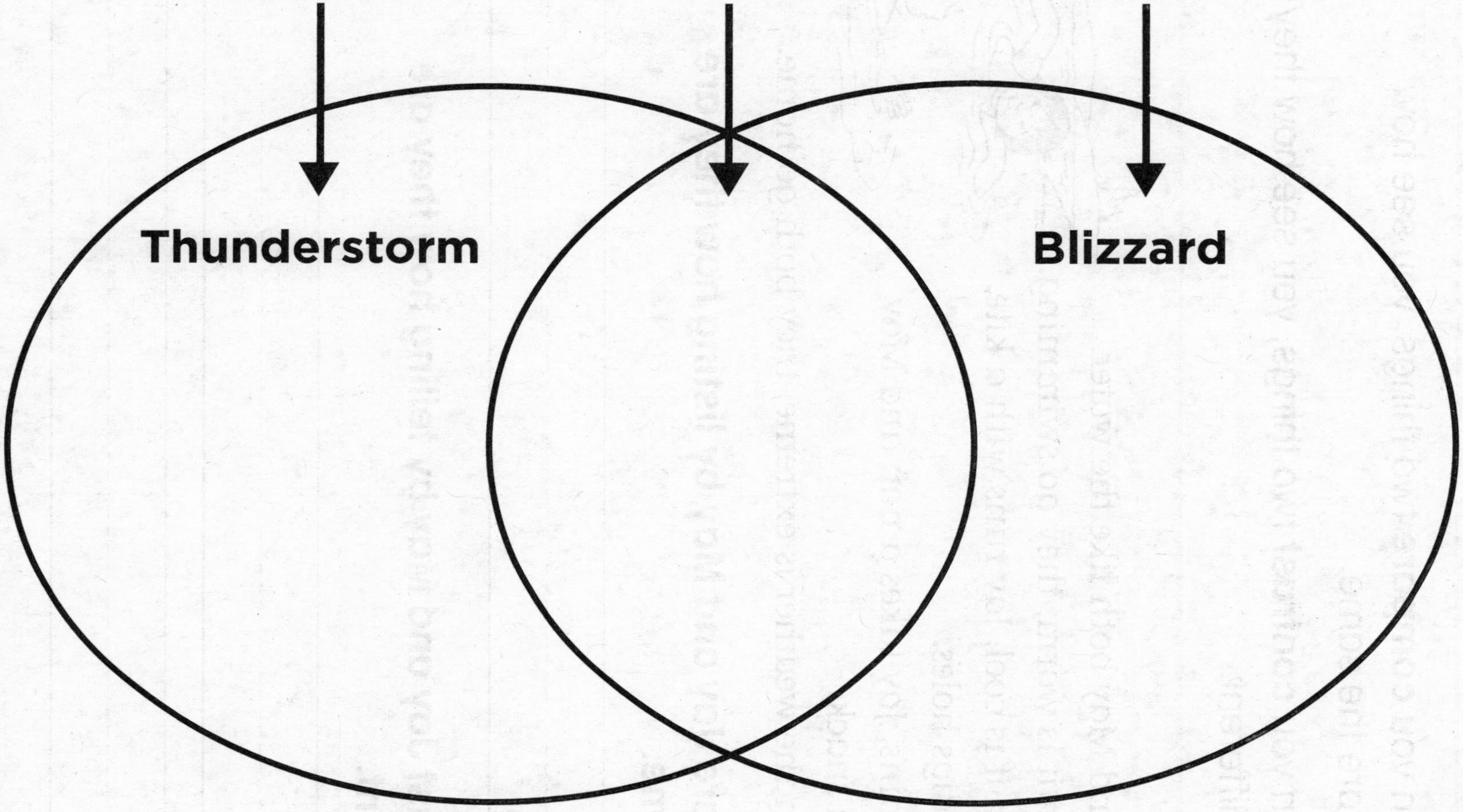

How does the Compare and Contrast Chart help you better understand Stormy Weather?

Name ____________________

When you **compare** two things, you see how they are the same.

When you **contrast** two things, you see how they are different.

Jay and May both like the water.
When it is warm, they go swimming.
When it is cool, Jay runs with a kite.
May digs holes.
If it rains, Jay takes a nap and May has a snack.
When the weather is extreme, they both go home.

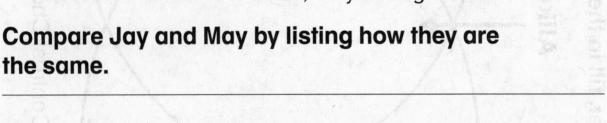

Compare Jay and May by listing how they are the same.

____

____

Contrast Jay and May by telling how they are different.

____

____

____

____

Name ______________________________

Words that have the same or almost the same meaning are called **synonyms**.

Synonyms:	smile	grin
	shine	glow

Words that have opposite meanings are called **antonyms**.

Antonyms:	new	old
	up	down

Read each row of words.

Circle the two words that are synonyms.

1. kind	happen	nice	ground
2. tiny	plant	big	little
3. happy	glad	mean	grow

Circle the two words that are antonyms.

4. dig	before	after	from
5. all	seeds	nothing	great
6. wet	care	again	dry

Name ______________________________

A **compound word** is made of two smaller words.

sun + set = **sunset**

down + hill = **downhill**

A. Match a word on the left to a word on the right to make a compound word. Then write the word.

1.  rain — flake — ______________

2.  snow — shine — ______________

3. sun — side — ______________

4. out — coat — ______________

B. Use a compound word in a sentence.

5. ______________________________

CA R 1.13 Read compound words and contractions.

Name ____________________

Circle the spelling word in each row.
Then write the spelling word on the line.

1. grunt get great ____________
2. fork from father ____________
3. crab cork coat ____________
4. kneel know never ____________
5. born block boys ____________
6. house hello horn ____________
7. people pork puppy ____________
8. cute chain corn ____________

CA **LC 1.8** Spell three- and four-letter short-vowel words and grade-level-appropriate sight words correctly.

Name ______________________________

Words with the same or almost the same meaning are **synonyms**. You can use a **dictionary** or a **thesaurus** to find synonyms. A thesaurus is a book that lists synonyms.

build to make something: Tim will **build** a house.
Synonyms: construct, make, create, form, and put together: Tim will **construct** a house.

Circle the two synonyms in each row that could complete the sentence.

1. That inventor has a clever _____.
   broken invention creation

2. The robot can _____.
   speak paper talk

3. The robot won a/an _____ in the contest.
   prize box award

Name ____

As I read, I will pay attention to phrasing.

Mike's class was at the art show.
07 "Always stay together, class," said Mrs. West.
14 "We don't want anyone to get lost."
21 The children stopped in one room. There were
29 many paintings to see.
33 "Come look at this one, Zack," said Mike.
41 Mike looked at the painting. There were people
49 in boats on a lake. Mike saw that one boat
59 had no one in it.
64 "I wish I could be in that boat," Mike said.
74 The next thing Mike knew, he was in the boat!
84 Mike put the paddles in the water and pulled.
93 Just then Mike heard Zack say,
99 "Come on, Mike. Let's go."
104 "Wait until I tell you what happened," said Mike. 113

Comprehension Check

1. Where did Mike and his class go?

2. What happened to Mike at the art show?

	Words Read	–	Number of Errors	=	Words Correct Score
First Read		–		=	
Second Read		–		=	

CA **R 1.16** Read aloud with fluency in a manner that sounds like natural speech.

Name ______________________________

A. Read about books. Find the book title. Write C above the title if it is written correctly. Write NC if it is not correct.

1. The book jack and the beanstalk is about Jack and a tiny seed that grows into a big plant. Jack is a good boy. But bad things happen when Jack goes up the tall plant.

2. I am reading Pick, pull, snap! It tells how to grow the plants shown in the book.

3. I liked the book Planting a Rainbow. The art in it is beautiful. Now I know how to help plants grow.

B. Write the wrong titles correctly on the lines.

____

____

____

A **card catalog** helps you find books in a library.

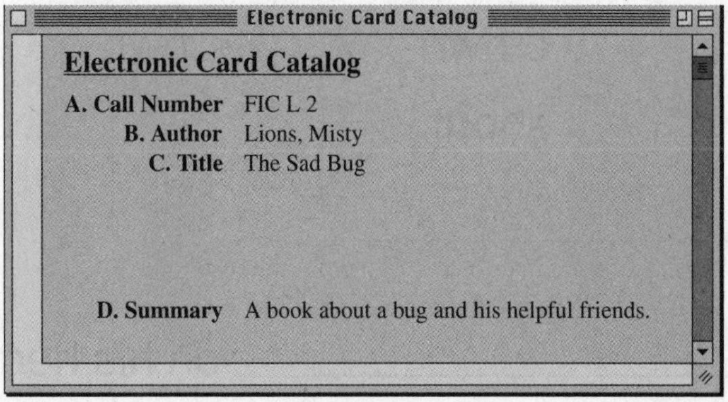
Electronic Card Catalog
Electronic Card Catalog
A. Call Number FIC L 2
B. Author Lions, Misty
C. Title The Sad Bug
D. Summary A book about a bug and his helpful friends.

A. These numbers show where you can find the book in the library.

B. author's name

C. the title of the book

D. what the book is about

Look at the computer screen. Then answer the questions.

1. What is the title? ______________________

2. What is the book about?

____

3. Who is the author? ______________________

4. Where can you find this book in the library? ____________

Name ______________________________

Use words from the box to complete the sentences.

cow	mouse	crown	clown
out	round	shout	

1. The king had a gold ________________ on his head.

2. The ball was red and ________________.

3. We can't go ________________ to play if it is raining.

4. The brown ________________ lives on a farm.

5. "Don't ________________ at me," yelled Ben.

6. The cat ran after the little ________________.

7. The funny ________________ had a red nose and big feet.

CA R 1.10 Generate the sounds from all the letters and letter patterns, including consonant blends and long- and short-vowel patterns (i.e., phonograms), and blend those sounds into recognizable words.

Name ______________________________

cow	how	town	out	mouse
mouth	born	fork	fall	sure

Write the spelling words with the same /ou/ sound as the word in the bug.

1. ____________________ **4.** ____________________

2. ____________________ **5.** ____________________

3. ____________________ **6.** ____________________

Write the spelling words you did not write above.

7. ____________________ **8.** ____________________

9. ____________________ **10.** ____________________

CA **LC 1.8** Spell three- and four-letter short-vowel words and grade-level-appropriate sight words correctly.

Name ______________________

Practice
High-Frequency Words/Vocabulary

Use the words from the box to complete the story.

against	fall	sure	below
yellow	orange	wondered	season

1. Look! Summer is gone. It is ______________.

2. It is the best ______________ of the year.

3. I am ______________ this will be a nice fall.

4. Leaves turn red, orange, and ______________.

5. I like the ______________ leaves better than the red or yellow ones.

6. She ______________ why the leaves fell.

CA R 1.11 Read common, irregular sight words (e.g., *the, have, said, come, give, of*).

Name ______________________________

As you read Happy Fall!, fill in the Sequence Chart.

First

↓

Next

↓

Then

↓

Last

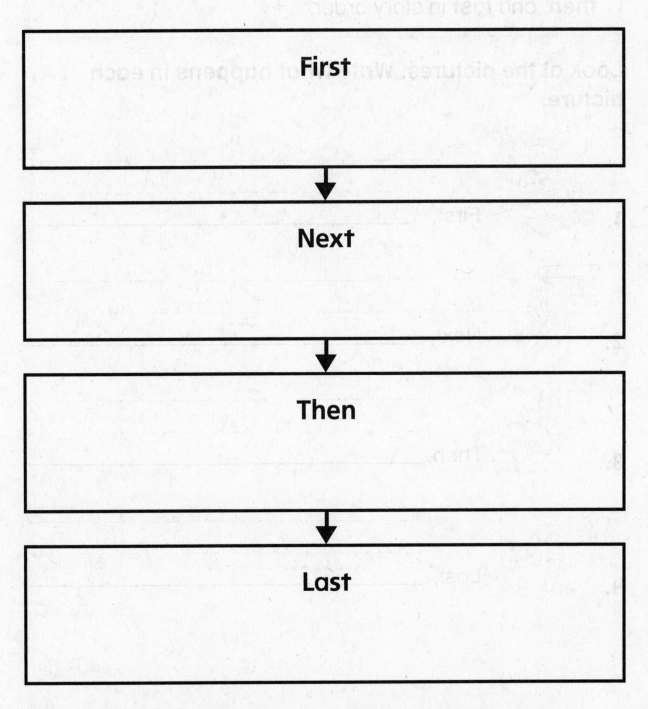

How does the Sequence Chart help you visualize what happens in Happy Fall!?

CA R 2.1 Identify text that uses sequence or other logical order.

Name ______________________

Practice

Comprehension: Sequence

The **sequence** tells what happens **first**, **next**, **then**, and **last** in story order.

Look at the pictures. Write what happens in each picture.

1. 

First, ______________________.

2. 

Next, ______________________.

3. 

Then, ______________________.

4. 

Last, ______________________.

CA R 2.1 Identify text that uses sequence or other logical order.

Name ______________________

An adjective tells about a noun. Some adjectives tell the color of something.

Example: **blue** sky

Find the color word in each sentence. Write it on the line.

1. Look at the yellow roses. ____________
2. Flick the black switch. ____________
3. Wait until the green light comes on. ____________
4. The clown has a red nose. ____________
5. Do you like my pink coat? ____________

Name ______________________________

A. Circle the word that names each picture.

1. 

mouse most

2. 

hose house

3. 

owl own

4. 

crowd crown

B. Use words from the box to complete the sentences.

cow	brown	round	mouse

5. The leaves on the ground were ______________.

6. The little ______________ looked for food.

Name ________________________

cow	how	town	out	mouse
mouth	born	fork	fall	sure

Change one letter to make a spelling word.
Write the spelling word on the line.

1. house ____________ 2. down ____________

3. hop ____________ 4. torn ____________

5. call ____________ 6. cot ____________

7. nut ____________ 8. month ____________

Look at the words you wrote above.
Circle the words that have the /ou/ sound.

CA **LC 1.8** Spell three- and four-letter short-vowel words and grade-level-appropriate sight words correctly.

Name ______________________________

A **base word** is the word that is left when you remove the **inflectional ending -ed** or **-ing**. You can use the base word to figure out the meaning of a word.

The teacher is **forming** the clay.
The base word is **form**.
form to give shape to something

Write the base word.

1. moved moving ____________

2. listening listened ____________

3. crashed crashing ____________

4. whistled whistling ____________

5. baked baking ____________

CA R 1.0 Word Analysis, Fluency, and Systematic Vocabulary Development

Name ____________________

As I read, I will pay attention to questions in the passage.

Look up at the blue sky in the day.
09 There is a big, round sun in the sky.
18 Do you see white clouds? The sun gives
26 us light. The sun is hot, so it makes us warm.
37 It helps plants grow, too.
42 Now, look up at the dark sky at night.
51 What is big and round and gives us light in
61 the night sky?
64 The moon! But some nights, we can not see it
74 at all.
76 The moon is bright in the sky but it is not hot.
88 It does not make us warm. There is a lot to
99 see in the night sky. 104

Comprehension Check

1. What is a difference between the sun and the moon?

2. What is the same about the sun and the moon?

	Words Read	–	Number of Errors	=	Words Correct Score
First Read		–		=	
Second Read		–		=	

CA **R 1.16** Read aloud with fluency in a manner that sounds like natural speech.

Name ______________________________

Read the story. Circle the color words.

The old black cat wasn't happy. He didn't like having gray mice in his house. "I am going to catch those gray mice," he said.

"We don't want that to happen," the little gray mice said. But the cat had soft feet. The mice couldn't tell when he was coming. So they made an alarm.

When the cat stepped on a red rug in front of their home, a green bell rang. The mice hid. "The black cat can't catch us," they said. "We aren't going to have to go away."

CA **LC 1.3** Identify and correctly use contractions (e.g., *isn't, aren't, can't, won't*) and singular possessive pronouns (e.g., *my/mine, his/her, hers, your/s*) in writing and speaking.

Name ____________________

Look at the diagram of a fire truck. Use the words from the box to complete the diagram. Write the words of the correct labels.

ladder	light	hose	cab

1. ____________________

2. ____________________

3. ____________________

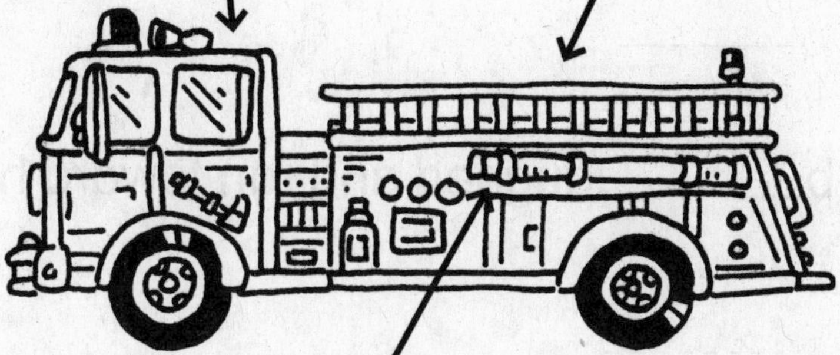

4. ____________________

Name ________________________________

Practice

Phonics: *oi, oy*

Read the words. The letters **oy** and **oi** stand for the vowel sounds in b**oy** and b**oi**l.

b**oy** b**oi**l

Read each sentence. Then complete the word by adding oi or oy.

1. The little child cried with j________ at the sight of the playful pups.

2. We will need more s________l for the new plants.

3. The little b________ laughed and ran toward his father.

4. Jen's new t________ toppled off the table and broke.

5. Mom has to put ________l in her car.

6. The water for our tea will b________l soon.

CA **R 1.4** Distinguish initial, medial, and final sounds in single-syllable words.

Name ______________________

joy	toy	boy	spoil	coin
join	town	mouse	eyes	enough

A. Complete the spelling word by writing the letters that make the /oi/ sound.

1. t ______

2. sp ______ l

3. c ______ n

4. j ______

5. j ______ n

6. b ______

B. Write the words that have the /ow/ sound.

7. ______

8. ______

CA **LC 1.8** Spell three- and four-letter short-vowel words and grade-level-appropriate sight words correctly.

Name ______________________

Choose a word from the box to finish each sentence. Then write the word on the line.

wild	learn	enough	air	cub	eyes

1. The tiger ______________ has a sister.

2. Soon the cubs will be old ______________ to hunt in the ______________.

3. They will ______________ from their mother.

4. They like the night ______________.

5. Their ______________ see well at night.

CA R 1.11 Read common, irregular sight words (e.g., *the, have, said, come, give, of*).

Name ____________________

As you read A Tiger Cub Grows Up, fill in the Compare and Contrast Chart.

Compare and Contrast	
Cub	**Grown-up**

How does the Compare and Contrast Chart help you better understand A Tiger Cub Grows Up?

Name ______________________

When you **compare**, you tell how two or more things are alike. When you **contrast**, you tell how things differ.

If something tells about "The Tiger," write it in that list. If something tells about "A Tiger Cub Grows Up," write it in that list. It is okay to write something in both lists.

lives in an animal park		speeds in the forest
has stripes		lives in the wild
poem	real story	drinks milk

"The Tiger" by Douglas Florian

1. ______________________ 2. ______________________

3. ______________________ 4. ______________________

"A Tiger Cub Grows Up" by Joan Hewitt

5. ______________________ 6. ______________________

7. ______________________ 8. ______________________

Name ______________________________

Some adjectives are words for numbers.

one	two	three	four	five
1	2	3	4	5
six	seven	eight	nine	ten
6	7	8	9	10

Circle the number word in each sentence. Draw a line to the picture it tells about.

1. The baby's bike has three wheels.

2. Pam's new bike has two wheels.

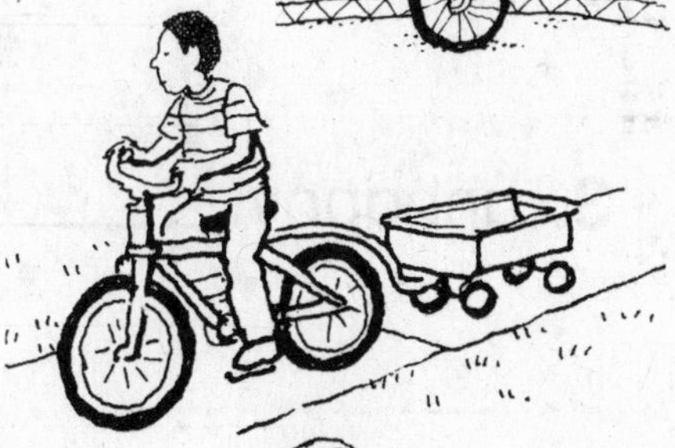

3. She rides a bike with one wheel.

4. There are four wheels on that bike.

5. See six wheels go round and round.

Name ______________________

A **prefix** is a word part you can add to the beginning of a base word to change the meaning of the word.

The prefix **re-** means **again**: **re** + pack = **re**pack

The prefix **un-** means **not** or **the opposite**: **un** + pack = **un**pack

Write the meaning of each of the following words:

1. reuse ______________________

2. refill ______________________

3. unhappy ______________________

4. unsafe ______________________

5. remake ______________________

6. untrue ______________________

Circle the spelling word in each row.
Then write the spelling word on the line.

1. space	spoil	shout	___
2. every	ease	eyes	___
3. boy	block	bear	___
4. engine	enough	energy	___
5. join	jaw	joke	___
6. jar	jump	joy	___
7. clues	chain	coin	___
8. tiny	toy	try	___

CA **LC 1.8** Spell three- and four-letter short-vowel words and grade-level-appropriate sight words correctly.

Name ________________________________

Context clues are words that help you figure out the meaning of a new word. Context clues may be found in the same sentence or in nearby sentences.

Use context clues to figure out the meaning of the underlined word. Fill in the correct circle.

1. The man displays the fruit. He wants to set the melon on the shelf.

   ○ throws away

   ○ shows or sets out

2. Jordan likes to go places. He enjoys taking the bus to the fruit stand.

   ○ likes

   ○ twists

3. Jordan's mom likes to relax at the park. She likes to sit and read.

   ○ finish quickly

   ○ rest

CA R 2.4 Use context to resolve ambiguities about word and sentence meanings.

Name ______________________________

As I read, I will pay attention to phrasing in the passage.

Who Were the Wright Brothers?

05 Orville and Wilbur Wright were inventors.
11 Their dream was to build a flying machine.
19 As children, they liked to find out how things
28 worked. As grown-ups, they worked in a bike
36 shop.
37 In 1900, the Wright brothers built a glider with
46 two wings. Each wing was covered with cloth.
54 They flew their glider like a kite.
61 After testing the glider, one brother got on the
70 glider. Then he would glide in the air.
78 The Wright brothers made and tested many
85 gliders. With each new discovery they made a
93 better glider. 95

Comprehension Check

1. Describe the glider the Wright brothers built.

2. How did the brothers fly their glider?

	Words Read	–	Number of Errors	=	Words Correct Score
First Read		–		=	
Second Read		–		=	

CA **R 1.16** Read aloud with fluency in a manner that sounds like natural speech.

Name ______________________________

Circle the mistakes in these sentences.

Then write the sentences correctly.

Write number words for numbers in each sentence.

Begin the names of days with capital letters.

1. I was 7 last saturday.

2. On sunday, the 4 of us see a show.

3. The man keeps 6 pins in the air.

4. I try hard on monday and tuesday.

Name ______________________________

Poets often use words in funny and interesting ways. The sounds of words can help express their meaning.

Read the poem. Find the fun words in each verse. Then write the words on the lines.

Bow-Wow

Bow-wow says the dog,
Mew, mew says the cat,
Grunt, grunt goes the hog,
And squeak goes the rat.

Whoo-oo says the owl,
Caw, caw says the crow,
Quack, quack says the duck,
And what cuckoos say, you know.

A fine song I have made,
To please you, my dear;
And if it's well-sung,
'Twill be charming to hear.

Name ____________________

Practice

Phonics: *oo* and *oo*

The letters **oo** can stand for the middle sound in m**oo**n.

Read the word and circle the picture for it.

1. noon

2. zoo

3. school

4. spoon

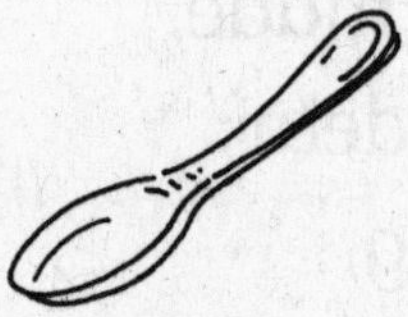

5. groom

CA **R 1.4** Distinguish initial, medial, and final sounds in single-syllable words.

Name ______________________

book	took	look	hood	cook
wood	toy	coin	mother	love

A. Circle the words that have the <u>oo</u> sound you hear in the word <u>good</u>.

B. Write the words you circled.

1. ______________ 4. ______________

2. ______________ 5. ______________

3. ______________ 6. ______________

CA **LC 1.8** Spell three- and four-letter short-vowel words and grade-level-appropriate sight words correctly.

Name ______________________

mother	four	always	firm
father	love	supposed	

Use words from the box to complete the sentences.

1. My mom is my ______________.

2. My dad is my ______________.

3. We ______________ each other.

4. We ______________ help each other.

5. We have ______________ cats.

6. I am ______________ to be good.

7. Sometimes they are ______________ with me.

Name ______________________________

As you read Olivia, fill in the Fantasy and Reality Chart.

Fantasy	Reality

How does the Fantasy and Reality Chart help you better understand Olivia?

Name ______________________

Reality is something that could really happen.

Fantasy is something that could not really happen.

Circle the sentences that show reality. Then underline the sentences that are fantasy.

1. A pig puts on a dress.
2. A pig paints.
3. A pig sleeps.
4. A pig goes to school.
5. A pig has a pet cat.
6. A pig sits in the mud.
7. A pig reads a book.
8. A pig has a mother.

Name ________________________

A sentence is made up of parts.

The **subject** of a sentence is the part that tells **whom** or **what** the sentence is about.

Example: An ant is on the leaf.
What is on the leaf?
An ant is. **An ant** is the subject.

Answer the question to find the subject of each sentence. Write the subject.

1. Flies have wings.

What has wings? ________________

2. That tiny spider made a big web.

What made a big web? ________________

3. Mr. Jones takes care of bees.

Who takes care of bees? ________________

4. Bees buzz around the hive.

What buzzes around the hive? ________________

Name ______________________________

When **'s** is added to a word, it means that something belongs to that person or thing.

Circle the correct word and write it on the line.

1. This is ______________ ball.

   Olivia   Olivia's

2. This is ______________ shirt.

   Ian's   Ian

3. This is ______________ bone.

   Perry   Perry's

4. This is the ______________ milk.

   cat's   cat

5. This is ______________ pencil.

   Mom   Mom's

Name ______________________________

**A. Find the spelling words in the puzzle.
Draw a circle around each word.**

f	p	i	v	h	q	j	s	n
u	j	s	l	o	x	m	i	y
p	x	b	o	o	k	f	u	s
m	i	e	v	d	y	v	a	g
q	n	m	e	j	s	p	e	u
e	m	o	t	h	e	r	i	v
i	f	j	o	n	u	c	q	p
g	m	s	o	f	w	o	o	d
l	o	o	k	i	v	o	x	j
p	s	g	j	m	i	k	n	f

B. Write the spelling words from the puzzle.

1. ____________________ **2.** ____________________

3. ____________________ **4.** ____________________

5. ____________________ **6.** ____________________

7. ____________________ **8.** ____________________

CA **LC 1.8** Spell three- and four-letter short-vowel words and grade-level-appropriate sight words correctly.

Name ______________________________

pretends plays or makes believe: Danny **pretends** he is an astronaut.

vanished disappeared: The sun **vanished** when the clouds came out.

observes sees or notices: A scientist **observes** things under a microscope.

inspecting looking at carefully: Mom is **inspecting** the house for dust.

Use a word from above to complete each sentence.

1. Kate thinks Matt ____________________ from the room!

2. She is ____________________ the room for clues.

3. He hides behind the toy box and ____________________ to be invisible.

4. Kate ____________________ many clues. She solves the mystery of the missing brother!

CA R 2.4 Use context to resolve ambiguities about word and sentence meanings.

Name ______________________________

As I read, I will pay attention to phrasing.

One night, Bird and Bear sat at the lake.
09 It was dark, and they were looking at the
18 moon.
19 “The moon looks flat,” said Bird.
25 “But I know it is round like a ball.”
34 “I would love to fly to the moon,” said Bear.
44 “You’re fooling. You can’t fly!” said Bird.
51 “Well, I could make a spaceship,” said Bear.
59 “Then I could fly.”
63 “Ha!” said Bird. “That would take too long.
71 Before you were done, I could fly to the moon
81 and back!”
83 “You can’t fly to the moon,” said Bear.
91 “It’s too far away in space.” 97

Comprehension Check

1. How will Bear fly to the moon?

2. How will Bird fly to the moon?

	Words Read	–	Number of Errors	=	Words Correct Score
First Read		–		=	
Second Read		–		=	

CA R 1.16 Read aloud with fluency in a manner that sounds like natural speech.

Name ________________________________

Read the story. Then write the letter or letters to tell how to fix each sentence.

Ⓐ Add a subject. Ⓒ Add an end mark.

Ⓑ Begin with a capital letter. Ⓓ Do not change.

(1) ant and White Bird didn't get along. (2) One day, Ant fell into the water (3) so White Bird dropped a leaf into the water (4) Got on the leaf. (5) The wind pushed the leaf to the sand. (6) Ant was saved. (7) What happened to Ant and White Bird (8) Have become good friends.

1. ________ 2. ________ 3. ________

4. ________ 5. ________ 6. ________

7. ________ 8. ________

CA LC 1.0 Written and Oral English Language Conventions

Name ____________________

Captions tell readers more about a photograph or picture.

Circle the caption that tells about the picture.

1. the talent show
the baseball game

2. the actors
the runners

3. my new dance
my new hat

4. the best singer
the best painting

5. the band
the swimming team

6. my sister's prize
my sister's bike

Name ______________________________

Read the words. What vowel sound do you hear? The letters **au** and **aw** stand for the vowel sound in P**au**l and p**aw**.

Circle the word that answers each riddle.

1. I am a large bird.

What am I? hawk haul

2. I grabbed with my claw.

What did I do? call caught

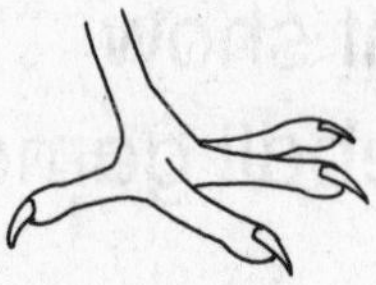

3. This is the start of the day.

What is it? dorm dawn

4. I like to do this in art class.

What is it? draw drink

5. A bird can use this to make a nest.

What is it? stand straw

CA **R 1.4** Distinguish initial, medial, and final sounds in single-syllable words.

Name ________________________

haul	claw	cause	paw	saw
dawn	book	took	along	nothing

Write the words with the /o/ sound.

1. ____________ **2.** ____________

3. ____________ **4.** ____________

5. ____________ **6.** ____________

7. ____________

Write the words with the /oo/ sound in look.

8. ____________ **9.** ____________

Write the word that does not have the /o/ sound or the /oo/ sound.

10. ____________

CA **LC 1.8** Spell three- and four-letter short-vowel words and grade-level-appropriate sight words correctly.

Practice

High-Frequency Words/Vocabulary

Name ______________________________

Use a word from the box to complete each sentence.

early	along	suddenly	errand
nothing	thought	instead	

1. We woke up ____________________ this morning.

2. We did an ____________________ for Mom.

3. There was ____________________ in the rice jar.

4. Mr. Ford ____________________ he had some.

5. We gave him three roses ____________________.

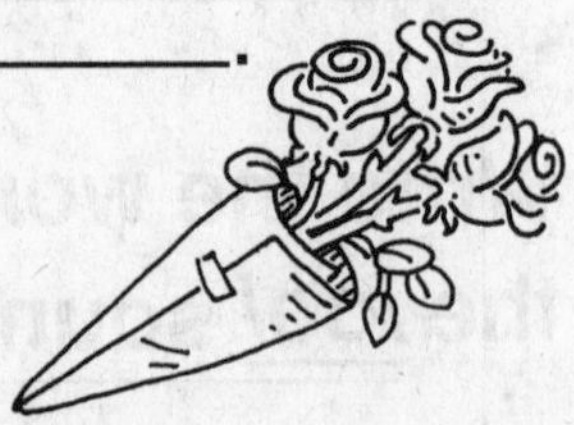

6. ____________________, it started to rain.

7. Mr. Ford told us to run ____________________.

CA R 1.0 Word Analysis, Fluency, and Systematic Vocabulary Development

Name ______________________________

As you read Whistle for Willie, fill in the Inference Chart.

Text Clues	What You Know	Inferences

How does the Inference Chart help you better understand Whistle for Willie?

Name ______________________________

Look at the picture. Then underline the sentence that is true.

1. 

Mark likes to play ball.

Mark wins the race.

Mark likes to ride his bike.

2. 

I can play catch.

I can see far away.

I can sing and dance.

3. 

I can play a game.

I can help Dad.

I can read a good book.

4. 

The water is fun.

The water is not deep.

The water is too cold.

5. 

I don't like to help.

I can help Mom make pancakes.

I don't know how to make pancakes.

Name ______________________________

A pronoun is a word that takes the place of a noun. Use the pronouns **she**, **he**, **it**, or **they** to take the place of one or more people or things in the subject of a sentence.

Mark and Manish have a dog. **They** have a dog.

Use the pronouns **her**, **him**, **it**, or **them** to take the place of one or more people or things in the object of a sentence.

I asked Zaneb for a book. I asked **her** for a book.

Circle the pronoun that takes the place of the underlined part of the sentence.

1. Janet likes to run and play. She It

2. Ari likes to throw the ball. They He

3. Misha writes a book report. her it

4. Anna and Geir sell hats. them it

5. Elena is my best friend. They She

Name ______________________________

Some pronouns go before a noun. Some stand alone.
This is **my** book. That pen is **mine.**

Use a pronoun from the box to complete the sentences. Use the underlined words as clues.

my	mine	ours	her	hers	theirs

1. This flute belongs to Patty. This flute is ____________.

2. That kite belongs to me. That kite is ____________.

3. This is Lisa's pet. This is ____________ pet.

4. This kitten belongs to Lee and Jack. This kitten is ____________.

Name ______________________________

Look at each set of words.
One word in each set is spelled correctly.
Use a pencil to fill in the circle in front of that word.

1. ○ ayer
○ aire
○ air

2. ○ cause
○ cawse
○ cose

3. ○ pawwe
○ pau
○ paw

4. ○ donn
○ dawn
○ daun

5. ○ sawe
○ saw
○ sauwe

6. ○ haul
○ hawl
○ hol

7. ○ clauw
○ clohe
○ claw

CA **LC 1.8** Spell three- and four-letter short-vowel words and grade-level-appropriate sight words correctly.

Name ______________________

Context clues are words that help you figure out the meaning of a new word. Context clues may be found in the same sentence or in nearby sentences.

Fill in the circle next to the correct meaning of the bold word. Use the underlined context clues to figure out the meaning of each word.

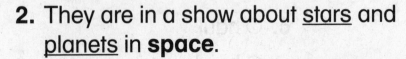

1. The girls are giggling and **fooling** around on the stage.
   ○ acting silly ○ cleaning

2. They are in a show about stars and planets in **space**.
   ○ the beach ○ a place where astronauts travel

3. The big **helmet** hides most of Seta's face.
   ○ boots ○ something that protects a person's head

4. Maria fell down. Her moon rocks **tumbled** off the stage.
   ○ dropped ○ dug

5. "These space boots make it hard to feel the **earth** under my feet," said Seta.
   ○ cold water ○ ground; also the planet where we live

CA R 2.4 Use context to resolve ambiguities about word and sentence meanings.

Name ____________________

As I read, I will pay attention to the phrasing.

Early one day, Jill tried to tie the laces on her shoes.
12 But she could not tie them.
18 "You will be able to do it one day soon,"
28 said Jill's mother. "Put on your shoes with the
37 straps." Then, she left to go shopping.
44 Along came Jill's sister, Molly. "Pretend the
51 laces are snakes. Tie the snakes together, like
59 this," said Molly.
62 Jill kept getting her snakes tied in knots.
70 "Put on your sandals," said Molly. "They do
78 not have laces."
81 Jill sat down and tried again. 87

Comprehension Check

1. What is Jill trying to do?

2. What animals does Molly tell Jill to pretend her laces are?

	Words Read	–	Number of Errors	=	Words Correct Score
First Read		–		=	
Second Read		–		=	

CA **R 1.16** Read aloud with fluency in a manner that sounds like natural speech.

Name ________________________

A sentence has a subject and a predicate.
Capitalize the name of a holiday.

Write

- **S** if a sentence is missing a subject.
- **P** if the sentence is missing a predicate.

Circle letters that should be capital in the name of a holiday.

1. Jack gave Dad a great gift for father's Day.

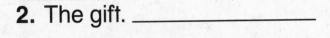

2. The gift. ________________

3. The two of them. ________________

4. Went to Mars on a rocket ship. ________________

5. They won't be back until thanksgiving. ________________

CA LC 1.0 Written and Oral English Language Conventions

Name ______________________________

A **list** is a series of things written in a certain order.

Dogs can do these jobs:

1.

2.

3.

4.

Read the question. Draw a line to the answer.

1. Which dog helps the blind?

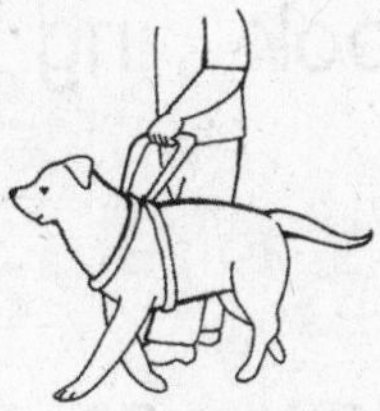

2. Which dog looks for clues?

3. Which dog watches sheep?

4. Which dog pulls a sled?

Name ______________________________

A **syllable** is a word part that has one vowel sound.

Put the two syllables together. Write the word on the line. Then match the word to the picture it names.

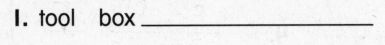

1. tool box ______________

2. paint ed ______________

3. cook ing ______________

4. slow er ______________

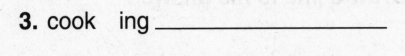

Connect the word parts to make a real job name. Write the job names on the lines.

farm	ist
art	er

5. ______________ **6.** ______________

CA R 1.0 Word Analysis, Fluency, and Systematic Vocabulary Development

Name ______________________________

dentist	happen	unpack	begin	lion
protect	saw	cause	goes	build

A. In each row put an X on the word that does not belong. Then write that spelling word.

1. saw	cause	dentist	____________
2. lion	goes	begin	____________
3. unpack	begin	saw	____________
4. protect	goes	build	____________

B. Write the spelling words that begin with b.

5. ____________ 6. ____________

Write the spelling words that have the same vowel sound as haul.

7. ____________ 8. ____________

CA LC 1.8 Spell three- and four-letter short-vowel words and grade-level-appropriate sight words correctly.

Name ______________________________

Use the words in the box to complete each sentence.

only	laugh	goes	build	ordinary	interesting

1. People like to ______________________.

2. It eats ______________________ the leaf.

3. She ______________________ in.

4. This bird is ______________________.

5. This bird is more ______________________.

6. Let's watch the bird ______________________ a nest.

CA **R 1.11** Read common, irregular sight words (e.g., *the, have, said, come, give, of*).

Name ______________________________

As you read Cool Jobs, fill in the Classify and Categorize Chart.

Classify and Categorize	
Jobs to Make Things	**Jobs That Help**

How does the Classify and Categorize Chart help you better understand Cool Jobs?

Name ______________________________

Write A if the sentence or sentences tell how two or more things are alike. Write D if the sentence or sentences tell how two or more things are different.

1. Ted has a black dog. May has a black cat. ______

2. Sam likes to sing and Mike likes to dance. ______

3. Dana and Karen have on blue pants. ______

4. Cara's flowers are red. Nia's flowers are pink. ______

5. Both toys are broken. ______

6. All of the babies are small. ______

CA R 2.0 Reading Comprehension

Name ______________________________

A **pronoun** is a word that takes the place of a noun.

Use the pronouns **he**, **she**, or **it** to take the place of one person or thing in the subject of a sentence.

Pete is a cook. **He** is a good cook.

Use the pronoun **they** to take the place of more than one person or thing in the subject.

The girls sing. **They** sing very well.

Circle the pronoun that takes the place of the underlined part of the sentence.

1. Mom and Dad work. They work hard.
2. Mr. Wall fixes cars. He fixes old cars.
3. Anna sells hats. She sells bags, too.
4. The two girls walk dogs. They walk all kinds of dogs.
5. My sister makes dresses. She makes doll dresses.

CA LC 1.0 Written and Oral English Language Conventions

Name ____________________

Practice

Structural Analysis: /âr/ *air, are, ear*

The letters ***air***, ***are***, and ***ear*** can make the same sound.

ch**air** sp**are** t**ear**

Write the words from the box that have the same vowel sound and spelling as the name of the picture.

fair	bear	dare	wear	pair	share

1. 
square
____________ ____________
____________ ____________

2. 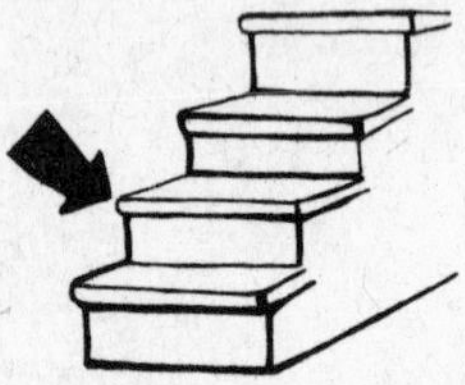
stair
____________ ____________
____________ ____________

3. 
pear
____________ ____________
____________ ____________

Name ______________________________

A. Circle the word in each row that is spelled correctly.

1.	lion	lyin	lian
2.	dentust	dentist	dennist
3.	build	biuld	bild
4.	bigin	begin	beggin
5.	cawes	caus	cause
6.	sau	sawe	saw

B. Write the spelling words that contain the short a sound.

7. ______________ 8. ______________

Write the spelling words that contain the long o sound.

9. ______________ 10. ______________

CA **LC 1.8** Spell three- and four-letter short-vowel words and grade-level-appropriate sight words correctly.

Name ______________________________

A **dictionary** is a book that gives the meaning of words. Some words have more than one meaning.

Read the definitions below.

flyer 1. a person who flies aircraft: The **flyer** did tricks in the small plane. **2.** a sheet of paper with information: The **flyer** gave the time and place of the sale.

model 1. a person who shows off clothes or other things: The **model** came down the runway in a beautiful dress. **2.** a small example of something: Jim built a ship **model**.

Choose the correct definition for the word. Fill in the circle.

1. flyer ○ paper with words ○ fix a roof
2. flyer ○ place in line ○ person in a plane
3. model ○ sit down ○ shows off clothes
4. model ○ small example ○ sandy beach

Use a word from above in a sentence.

____

____

Name ______________________________

As I read, I will pay attention to phrasing.

Some people fly sightseeing planes.
05 Sightseeing planes fly low to the ground.
12 That way, people on the plane can see all
21 the sights.
23 Some people fly helicopters. A helicopter is
30 different from a plane. Helicopters
35 can fly forward and fly backward.
41 Also, they can turn in a circle
48 and stay still in the air.
54 There are places where only helicopters
60 can fly. There are places where
66 planes cannot go. 69

Comprehension Check

1. Why do sightseeing planes fly low to the ground?

2. In what directions can helicopters fly?

	Words Read	–	Number of Errors	=	Words Correct Score
First Read		–		=	
Second Read		–		=	

CA R 1.16 Read aloud with fluency in a manner that sounds like natural speech.

Name ______________________________

Correct the letter. Cross out the underlined words. Write a pronoun to take their place in the space above. Add missing commas.

March 14 1874

Dear Will,

Our new house is done. Our new house is made of logs. Dad used tree trunks to make the logs. Dad had to cut down lots of trees.

My sister Kate has her own room now. My sister Kate is very happy about that.

Next week, Mom and Dad will open their shop in Dows Iowa. Mom and Dad will sell food, cloth, and other goods.

Your best friend

Hans

Name ______________________________

You can use the Internet to find out about a topic. Put important words, or keywords, in the search box. Then hit GO, and a list of links will pop up.

Write the keywords you would type in the search box to look up the following:

1. You want to know more about the moon. ______________________

2. You want to find out about places to see in New York. ______________________

3. You want to know more about the animal you like best. ______________________

4. You want to find out about a job you would like. ______________________

Name ______________________

A **syllable** is a word part that has one vowel sound. Some words have more than one syllable.

A. Put the two syllables together. Write the word on the line. Then match the word to the picture it names.

1. short est ______________________

2. hill y ______________________

3. in sect ______________________

4. lift ing ______________________

B. Circle the two words in the sentence that have two syllables. Write the words on the lines.

The mice were looking for bugs in the meadow.

5. ______________________ 6. ______________________

Name ______________________

jumping	looking	waiting	stopping	running
planning	dentist	lion	before	been

A. Read each row of words. Put an X on the word that does not belong.

1. jumping waiting lion
2. been looking stopping
3. planning before waiting
4. dentist jumping running

B. Write the spelling words that have two n's in the middle.

5. ______________ 6. ______________

Write the spelling word that has only one syllable.

7. ______________

CA LC 1.8 Spell three- and four-letter short-vowel words and grade-level-appropriate sight words correctly.

Name ______________________

Circle the word that completes each sentence. Then write the word on the line.

1. Where has the cat ____________?
   done gone

2. The girls have ____________ best friends for years.
   been are

3. Let's keep ____________ for the missing dog.
   sending searching

4. We must look for ____________.
   close clues

5. I can't see it. It must be ____________.
   invisible instead

6. "I saw the keys ____________ we left," said Mom.
   other before

CA **R 1.11** Read common, irregular sight words (e.g., *the, have, said, come, give, of*).

Name ____________________________

As you read Dot and Jabber and the Big Bug Mystery, fill in the Predictions Chart.

What I Predict	What Happens

How does the information you wrote in this Predictions Chart help you better understand Dot and Jabber and the Big Bug Mystery?

Name ______________________________

In a **prediction**, you tell what you think will happen next.

Read each story. Then complete the sentence to tell what could happen next.

1. The ship takes off. It is flying to the moon.
It will

______________________________.

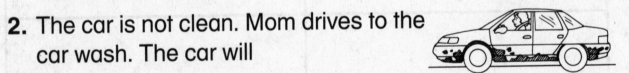

2. The car is not clean. Mom drives to the car wash. The car will

______________________________.

3. It is a windy day. We have kites.
We will

______________________________.

4. Dad brings home a bag full of food.
He cooks the food. We will

______________________________.

Name ________________________

The words **I** and **me** are pronouns.

Use **I** in the subject of a sentence.

Use **me** in the predicate of a sentence.

Examples: **I** have a book about Baby Bird.
Mom gave **me** the book.

Write I in the subject.

1. ______________ am Baby Bird.

2. My sisters and ______________ just hatched.

3. ______________ want some food.

Write me in the predicate.

4. Mom feeds worms to ______________.

5. She keeps ______________ warm in the nest.

6. Soon, Dad will show ______________ how to fly.

Name ______________________________

Contractions combine two words. The **apostrophe** (') takes the place of any missing letters.

we + will = **we'll** I + am = **I'm** you + have = **you've**

A. Write the contraction for the two words.

1. we + have = ____________

2. he + will = ____________

3. I + am = ____________

4. she + will = ____________

B. Use the contractions to complete the sentences.

5. ____________ scratching my itch.

6. ____________ be glad when spring is here.

CA R 1.0 Word Analysis, Fluency, and Systematic Vocabulary Development

Name ______________________________

A. Circle the word in each row that is spelled correctly.

1. jumping	jumpng	jumpeing
2. stoppng	stoping	stopping
3. wating	waiting	wayting
4. planning	planeing	planeng
5. luuking	loocking	looking
6. runnig	running	runing

B. Write the spelling words that do NOT end in ing.

7. ______________________ 8. ______________________

9. ______________________ 10. ______________________

CA LC 1.8 Spell three- and four-letter short-vowel words and grade-level-appropriate sight words correctly.

Name ______________________

An **inflected verb** is a verb with an ending. When you remove the **-ing** or **-ed** ending, you are left with the base word.

inflected verb	**base word**
splash**ing**	splash
splash**ed**	splash

Write the ending. Then write the base word. The first one is done for you.

1. opened ___ed___ ___open___
2. chewing ________ ________
3. pointed ________ ________
4. crawling ________ ________
5. roaring ________ ________
6. talked ________ ________

Name ________________________________

As I read, I will pay attention to phrasing in the story.

Meena looked out at the birds that had
08 come to her backyard.
12 "Look at how great they are," Meena said.
20 "I want them to stay, not fly away."
28 "Well, we can make a birdhouse," Mama
35 said. "It would be welcoming and then the
43 birds might not leave."
47 "Wow, that's a great idea," said Meena. "Let's
55 make it this afternoon."
59 Meena called her friends Wendy and Mark
66 to help. Soon Wendy and Mark came over.
74 While Wendy took out paper and paints, Mark
82 took out wood and glue. And Meena put out
91 foil stickers. 93

Comprehension Check

1. Why does Meena want to build a birdhouse?

2. Do you think Meena, Wendy, and Mark are good friends?

	Words Read	–	Number of Errors	=	Words Correct Score
First Read		–		=	
Second Read		–		=	

CA **R 1.16** Read aloud with fluency in a manner that sounds like natural speech.

Use **I** in the subject of a sentence.

Use **me** in the predicate of a sentence.

Always capitalize the pronoun **I**.

Find mistakes in the play. Circle the pronoun I if it is not written correctly. Make an X on I or me if it is not used correctly.

1. CUBBY: Mama catches fish for I.

   Sometimes, i eat berries, too.

   I am getting taller and stronger.

2. NUBBY: Me want to learn to fish, Mama.

   Cubby and i are growing up.

3. MAMA: i will teach you to fish, sons.

   You will watch me and learn.

Name ___________________________

A **head** tells what information is in a section of an article or story.

A. Read the article about spiders.

Spiders

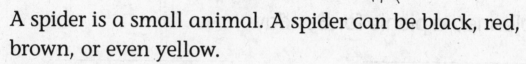

A spider is a small animal. A spider can be black, red, brown, or even yellow.

The Body of a Spider

A spider has 2 body parts. It also has 8 legs. An insect has only 6 legs.

The Home of a Spider

A spider lives in a web. It spins a sticky web. When a bug flies into the web, it gets stuck. Then the spider eats it.

B. Answer the questions about the article.

1. Circle the two heads that tell what information is in the sections.
2. Write one fact from each section.

____

____

Name ______________________________

Some words have more than one **syllable**, or word part.

Read each sentence. Circle the two words with two syllables. Write the words on the lines.

Meg planned a picnic for Sunday.

1. ______________ 2. ______________

She asked seven children to come.

3. ______________ 4. ______________

She made peanut butter snacks.

5. ______________ 6. ______________

Her puppy came along, too.

7. ______________ 8. ______________

Name ________________________________

lunchtime	daydream	shortcake	pancakes	picnic
perform	jumping	running	certain	minutes

Read each row of words. Put an X on the word that does not belong.

1. pancakes	shortcake	certain
2. lunchtime	perform	shortcake
3. jumping	daydream	running
4. daydream	lunchtime	jumping
5. picnic	perform	running
6. daydream	lunchtime	minutes

CA **LC 1.8** Spell three- and four-letter short-vowel words and grade-level-appropriate sight words correctly.

Name ____________________

straight	certain	begin	brought
minutes	around	daydream	cancel

Choose the correct word from the box and write it on the line.

1. Ann had a ____________________.

2. How did the dream ____________________?

3. A cat ____________________ Ann a beautiful car.

4. Ann drove the car ____________________ town.

5. Then she went ____________________ back home.

Name ______________________________

As you read Super Oscar, fill in the Story Chart.

Characters

Setting

Beginning

↓

Middle

↓

End

How does the information you wrote in this Story Chart help you retell Super Oscar?

CA **R 3.1** Identify and describe the elements of plot, setting, and character(s) in a story, as well as the story's beginning, middle, and ending.

Name ______________________________

The **characters** are the people or animals in a story.

The **setting** is where the story happens.

The **plot** is what happens.

Look at the pictures. Answer the questions about the characters, setting, and plot.

1. Who is the story about? ______________________________

2. Where does the story happen? ______________________________

3. What happens in the middle? ______________________________

4. What happens at the end? ______________________________

CA **R 3.1** Identify and describe the elements of plot, setting, and character(s) in a story, as well as the story's beginning, middle, and ending.

Name ______________________________

Parts of two sentences are sometimes the same.

Use **and** to join two sentences that have parts that are the same. Maria makes a fort. Ed makes a fort.

Maria and Ed make a fort.

Circle parts that are the same.
Use and to join the sentences.
Write the new sentence.

1. Mom hammers. Mom saws.

   Mom ______________________________.

2. Maria hauls wood. Ed hauls wood.

   ______________________________ haul wood.

3. Maria sands. Maria paints.

   Maria ______________________________.

4. Ed gets a mop. Ed gets a broom.

   Ed gets ______________________________.

5. Nana helps. Papa helps.

   ______________________________ help.

CA LC 1.0 Written and Oral English Language Conventions

Name ______________________________

A **compound word** is made up of two small words.

pop + corn = **popcorn**

pea + nuts = **peanuts**

A. Match a word on the left to a word on the right to make a compound word. Then write the word.

1. pan end ______________

2. camp dream ______________

3. day cakes ______________

4. week ground ______________

B. Use one compound word in a sentence.

5. ______________________________

CA R 1.13 Read compound words and contractions.

Name ______________________________

Practice

Spelling: Two-Syllable Words

A. Circle the word in each row that is spelled correctly.

1. piknik piknic picnic

2. certain sertin certian

3. perfrom perform purfrum

4. jumping jumpig jumpping

5. running runing runng

6. minuts minutes minuttes

B. Write the spelling words that are compound words.

7. ______________ 8. ______________

9. ______________ 10. ______________

CA LC 1.8 Spell three- and four-letter short-vowel words and grade-level-appropriate sight words correctly.

Practice

Vocabulary Strategy: Context Clues

Name ______________________________

Use the underlined context clues to figure out the meaning of the word in bold letters. Then match the word to its meaning. Write the correct letter on the line.

a. moved round and round
b. came back
c. tapped gently
d. to keep safe
e. a bridge that can be raised and lowered

1. The royal family **returned** home from a trip to the countryside. ____

2. The king, queen, and prince crossed over the **drawbridge** toward the castle. ____

3. The happy queen kissed the prince and **patted** him on the head. ____

4. Water from the river **swirled** in the moat. ____

5. The moat and the drawbridge **protect** the castle from strangers. ____

CA **R 2.4** Use context to resolve ambiguities about word and sentence meanings.

Name ______________________________

Practice

Fluency: Choral Read: Phrasing

As I read, I will pay attention to phrasing in the story.

Strawberries are easy plants to grow.
06 1. First, find a place that gets at least six hours
16 of sun.
18 2. Next, dig holes for the little plants. Put the
27 holes 12 inches apart. They should not be
35 crowded together.
37 3. Put the plants in the holes. Press the soil
46 around each plant. Make sure the soil covers
54 the tops of the roots.
59 4. Then, water the plants.
63 5. Pick the strawberries when they are ripe.
70 Animals like strawberries. As your plants grow,
77 you will need to watch for animals. Birds
85 and bugs eat strawberry plants. 90

Comprehension Check

1. Is it easy or hard to grow strawberries?

2. What do strawberries need to grow?

	Words Read	–	Number of Errors	=	Words Correct Score
First Read		–		=	
Second Read		–		=	

CA **R 1.16** Read aloud with fluency in a manner that sounds like natural speech.

Name ________________________________

Use **and** to make two sentences into one.

Always capitalize the pronoun **I**.

Always capitalize proper nouns.

Circle letters that should be capital letters. Underline the parts of the sentences that should be joined. Write the new sentences.

1. mom goes to sandy point beach.
i go to sandy point beach.

____

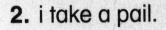

2. i take a pail.
i take a scoop.

____

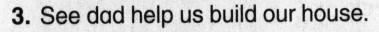

3. See dad help us build our house.
See leon help us build our house.

____

Name ______________________________

Some poems have a **rhyming pattern**.

In some poems, the second line of a verse rhymes with the fourth line.

A. Circle the two rhyming words in each poem.

The sun is out.
What a fine day!
Will you come out with me
And play?

I saw a seed
Fall to the ground.
It never made
A sound.

You want to play ball,
But what I'd like
Is to ride round and round
On my brand new bike.

I look up at
The sky at night,
And watch the stars
That shine so bright.

B. Think of more rhyming pairs. Write the pairs below.

1. ______________________ ______________________

2. ______________________ ______________________